STEPHEN WALSH

Heartache Spoken Here

VIKING

VIKING

Published by the Penguin Group
Penguin Books Ltd, 27 Wrights Lane, London W8 5TZ, England
Penguin Books USA Inc., 375 Hudson Street, New York, New York 10014, USA
Penguin Books Australia Ltd, Ringwood, Victoria, Australia
Penguin Books Canada Ltd, 10 Alcorn Avenue, Toronto, Ontario, Canada M4V 3B2
Penguin Books (NZ) Ltd, 182–190 Wairau Road, Auckland 10, New Zealand

Penguin Books Ltd, Registered Offices: Harmondsworth, Middlesex, England

First published 1997
10 9 8 7 6 5 4 3 2 1

The author and publishers wish to thank the following for permission to reprint
copyright material:
Lyrics from 'A Good Year for the Roses' by Jerry Chestnut, reproduced by permission
   of Sony Music Publishing.
Lyrics from 'Stand By Your Man' by Tammy Wynette and Billy Sherrill © 1968,
   EMI Al Gallico Music Corp., USA. Reproduced by permission of EMI Music
   Publishing Ltd, London WC2H 0EA.
Lyrics from 'Brown to Blue' by Mathis/Franks/Jones reproduced by permission of
   Campbell Connelly & Co. Limited.
Lyrics from 'Margaritaville' by Jimmy Buffet © PolyGram Music Publishing Ltd.
   Reproduced by permission of the publisher.
Lyrics from 'All the Best' by John Prine, published by Weona Music (administered by
   Bug Music).
Lyrics from 'If Only She Hadn't Been Her' and 'Please, Tammy' by Debra Paris © 1996;
   'Through The Eyes of a Cowboy' by A. Mc Elhill and Steve James © 1996;
   'Mr Johns' by Phil Parry © 1996, all reproduced by permission of the authors.

Set in 10/14pt Monotype Century Schoolbook
Typeset by Rowland Phototypesetting Ltd, Bury St Edmunds, Suffolk
Printed in Great Britain by Clays Ltd, St Ives plc

A CIP catalogue record for this book is available from the British Library

ISBN 0-670-86890-6

Contents

For my daughter, Judith,
the most beautiful girl in the world

There is a general place in the brain, I think, reserved for 'melancholy of relationships past'. It grows and prospers as life progresses, forcing you finally, against your grain, to listen to country music.

KARY MULLIS, BIOLOGY LAUREATE
NOBEL PRIZE LECTURE, STOCKHOLM, 1993

AUTHOR'S NOTE

The time sequence of some of the events described in this book has been altered.

The Last Word in Lonesome is Me

This is the story of two romances.

The first is my ex-wife's. Last year she took up and moved in with the Greek who worked in the next office. Finding myself alone, I allowed a flirtation that had long flickered at the edge of my life to blossom into love. The object of my affection is blessed with real feeling, knows what a heartbreak is and, unlike my wife, stands by her man. I confess it – I have been spending too much time with Country and Western music.

What happens if you play a country song backwards?

You'll want to know how these things began. How did she – I'll call her Ruby, after the woman who took her love to town – come to squeak for the Greek? And how did I, after years of unadulterated fidelity to rock and pop, come to acquire a healthy portion of the works of Johnny Paycheck? I suppose – though I would say this, wouldn't I? – that Ruby's is an everyday story of suburban adultery. But mine? Well, mine felt like the love that they say everyone has once in their lives.

Ruby's starts, I imagine, in the canteen. It's the latest itch in a long, unscratched series; but even left unscratched, the itch still comes back, and she's begun to be aware that a persistent itch probably equals an unhappy marriage. So this itch is a bit more serious from the off, and, as she gazes at the Greek's tanned brow, she begins to wonder, to look a little further in and

1

– though I would say this, wouldn't I? – a little further down. They talk. Conversation is at first innocent, then, as common ground is found, aware; soon they're finding ways to turn a group into a pair. Walks in the park become fanciful, fantasy-ful, become walks around the world, and an idea becomes a conviction: *my husband just doesn't touch me like you do . . .*

And me? Well – a crowded room, of course; the record-shop. I'm bored with my ten-year marriage to the rock and pop section – it just doesn't touch me – and ripe for some adulterous excitement – I mean, I like rock, I admire it, maybe I even love it – I'm just not passionate about it. I spy the *Greatest Hits of George Jones* in the bargain-bin and my heart leaps with the shock of the new. But wait – those fluffy sideburns, that bright lemon blazer – could I give up the comfortable custom of decades to spend my life with *that*? My fears melt away before George's subtle persuasions. I carry the cassette home in the pocket next to my heart, and before I know it I'm telling my friends about it, not to mention rooting round every record sale in town humming 'Am I That Easy to Forget?'

The answer to George's question is yes as far as Ruby is concerned. She's humming a different tune, or maybe just – particularly in that part of her which I have apparently been unable to touch these recent years – humming. The words of her song touch her like a warm wind off the Aegean, and getting out of a humdrum marriage is starting to feel like something that requires a bit of heroism. He's Odysseus, she's Penelope; he's Hector, she's Andromache; he's Paris, sailing across the seas to woo a Helen trapped in a loveless union. So what if I, with a blend of misogyny and xenophobia that I've recently picked up from somewhere and which I fool myself into thinking is an expression of love of some kind, accuse her of being Shirley Valentine being sung to on the beach by a waiter who looks like Demis Roussos? *She* knows the real words, and they're for her ears only.

But however much I think I care, I don't care, because I too am on the receiving end of winsome words. As my C&W collection expands, so does my stock of lyrical felicities, and my particular verbal caresses – the hook-line wizardry of Country and Western's wittiest – are of a purer poetry. I lap them up. 'I'll Never Get Out of This World Alive', 'All My Ex-es Live in Texas', 'She's Acting Single – I'm Drinking Doubles', 'The Wino and I Know', 'My Arms Stay Open All Night', 'What I Wouldn't Take Is More than She Could Give', 'Here's a Quarter – Call Someone Who Cares', 'Nobody in His Right Mind Would Have Left', 'I Ain't Sharin' Sharon', 'Don't Give Candy to a Stranger', 'Drop-Kick Me, Jesus, Through the Goal-Posts of Life', 'My Tears Have Washed "I Love You" from the Blackboard of My Heart'. A hundred, a thousand others. And these too are unique, for my ears only. They have to be – Ruby won't let me play them in the house.

At least she's still in the house at this stage. However, she's started to take work-time time-outs to do whatever she's doing with him; the sort of thing you only find out about afterwards, the sort of thing that everybody knows about; everybody except you. How our car is parked outside his house on a day his flatmates get locked out. (There's a country song called 'That Ain't My Truck in Her Drive'; but 'That *Is* My Truck in *His* Drive'? It's not the same.) Not having noticed, I don't mind; because when 'She's not at her desk, shall I get her to call you?' I am not at my (home-based) desk either. No, I am downstairs, listening with the anxiety of a mother crooning over a wailing child to Hank Williams wheezing his tubercular way through 'Cold, Cold Heart'.

And so on and so forth. By the time she's taken to dallying on the way home, popping in first for a quick, then for a slow drink, first at the staff club and then at pubs where she knows that no one I know ever goes, I too am out, living in a world of beer-halls, of juke-joints, of out-of-town honky-tonks; I'm out of my mind in my mind. My world is full of honky-tonk angels, of tears in my beer, of warm beer and cold women, of (subsequent) wrecks on the highway. I don't even register that she's started to check that she has her best underwear on of a morning – 'Just in case,' she probably says to herself, pulling out the bright white M&S stuff I've dutifully laundered for her – because I am pulling out, polishing up and proudly pulling on the brown leather boots (pointed toes, stacked heels, spirograph flower-pattern up the calves) I picked up in America a year before.

So, almost before I know it, and certainly before I expect it, she's decided to go. The Greek is all right in the night, so it's too late for Relate. Her bags are packed and ready to go and she's standing there outside my door – well, occasions like this are made for country music, and the only possible soundtrack is a full-blown pedal-steel one. I can't quite bring myself to play any of the funny ones all of a sudden ('My Uncle Used to Love Me But She Died' doesn't feel like quite the thing), but good ol' George goes on, and poor ol' Hank goes on, and the less-known but stupendously lonesome John Prine goes on; 33 rpm, it seems, is 'The Speed of the Sound of Loneliness'. And once she's gone – actually gone, after all the false starts and the doubts and the hesitations and the battles with ambition and mediocrity – once she's gone I can abandon my sternly set jaw-line, my *I-don't-give-a-fuck-you'll-be-sorry* pugnacity, and the whole screwed-up, repressed knot of emotions and feelings and responses can unwind as I listen to a whole train of truly fine songs that speak plainly of being in this position: 'Why Don't You Love Me Like You Used to Do?', 'Please Please Baby', 'Your Cheatin' Heart (Will Make You Weep)', 'If Heartaches Are the Fashion (Then I Guess that I'm in Style)', 'From Now On, Call Me Lonesome', 'Oh, Lonesome Me', 'I'm So Lonesome I Could Cry' . . . and at last I can stop trying to stop something that I don't want to happen happening; at last, away from fear and loss and inconvenience, I can find the tears I should probably have cried a lot, lot earlier.

Sometime soon after that – I can't pretend it was at that very moment of departure, but it wasn't very long afterwards – an old C&W-mocking joke came back to me. *Q. What happens if you play a country song backwards? A. Your truck starts, your dog gets resurrected and your wife comes back*. And I realized that the hard-times theme – that wailing note of pain and heartache – that lives in the best country music had always been visible to me, but that I had never really felt it. After all, I wasn't born into poverty in the Southern States, nor was my father a cotton-picker, nor did I grow up listening to Saturday night prime-time wireless. Up to the point that Ruby walked out that door, I didn't have the credentials to be a true C&W fiend. My name wasn't Hank (or, for that matter, Sue); I hadn't spent the daytimes of my youth cropping shares, or my night-times listening to a crackling wireless; my grandpa hadn't slept with my sister, and my parents hadn't drunk corn whisky or cheated or beat each other (or me) up.

But as I listened to George and Hank and John pouring out those deeply balming heartache numbers, it suddenly seemed clear that in the moment of my greatest pain had come a moment of joy. In the moment of my being dumped on – of being emotionally cheated, of being spiritually beaten up – I had suddenly developed the vestiges of a C&W life. I was suddenly the victim of a real-life 'D-I-V-O-R-C-E'; I was suddenly alone and forsaken; I was suddenly a man who knew for sure that once in a while everybody's baby gets the urge to roam and that everybody's baby but mine was coming home. And it was that combination of feelings – the discovery of where the soul of country music lay, that it really did have the emotional base that people claimed for it, and that I was suddenly qualified and experienced and graduated in it – that sent me out on the journeys amongst Country and Western people that this book describes.

It seemed to me that somewhere amongst these people for whom words about heartache are a first language, there must be the sort of expertise I needed to get me through a giddy stage in my life which, whatever my flippancy and inclination to retreat into comedy – I am a man, after all – was confusingly

5

painful and painfully confusing. I decided, in that time of pain and confusion, to get out on to the lonesome highway, to go anywhere where a real heart could be found beating behind a checked shirt. I wanted to talk to C&W people about themselves, about their lives, about how they came to be listening or driving or drinking or slow-waltzing to the sound of melancholy music; I wanted to find out about what had happened to them, and, from their expertise, to find out what would happen to me; I wanted to find out about what had happened to me and to my marriage.

It was a funny year for marriage. I went to three weddings in the course of it, and by the end of it, two of the couples had separated. In the course of the year Fergie and Andrew and Nelson and Winnie and a hundred thousand humdrum others untied the knot. In the course of the year another princess went on television to plead for some attention to be paid to her side of the marital story and showed inadvertently, as she spouted the bitter tears of the marginalized, why something sensible had to be done with the divorce laws; and in the course of the year, when the Lord Chancellor tried to do something sensible with the divorce laws, a bunch of right-wingers, spouting stuff about family values, watered his changes down so that his initial proposals lost all their benevolent completeness. More significantly for me, it was a year in which the whole process that follows separation – that whole, maddening untying which takes those already torn asunder and forces them together to discuss every aspect of their lives – went on. The year of my travels was also the year of my divorce, and – here's a real everyday story for you – it was a year that saw an amicable separation descend into acrimony.

So as well as being a story of two romances, this is also the story of two journeys. The first is the literal one. In a year in the velour saddle of my VW camper-van I travelled hundreds and hundreds of miles, from the Highlands to Hampshire, from Ireland to Suffolk, willing to stop off in any place where stetsons are worn and where they can put a sign in the window saying *Heartache Spoken Here*. Out on that lonely road I had time to look hard at myself, and I found, in this year, that I was bitter, twisted, savage, vicious; open, vulnerable, straight, fair; cagey, evasive, slippery, deceitful; reconciled, generous, true, honest. The second journey took me, in other words, into the frontier country of the heart; that altogether weird land known as humanity in distress, where, every year, hundreds of thousands of people find themselves when they argue and fight and split and separate and react in a million ways to the daily business of heartache. And at the end of the road of that journey – if only I had been able to see it – was another, better, maturer love. Maybe it was there all the time; maybe I had to travel that particular road to find it. But that, as they say, is another story.

Honey – if I felt as good as you look, I'd be dancing . . .

Country music is good on divorces, not so good on weddings. Like me. So you don't need to know much about my marriage, except that it began on a dull Tuesday in December and ended, perversely, on a warm August Saturday; that although it was probably, in retrospect, not something made in heaven, it lasted seven years; that although it wasn't really a very passionate relationship it produced two children; and that, in spite of everything anyone said at the time, it was no one's fault in the end. Oh, and that we went to Nashville for our honeymoon.

Well, not a honeymoon exactly; but we hadn't had one, after that December Tuesday; we hadn't quite got round to organizing one, just like we hadn't got round to organizing quite a lot of things, such as our thoughts on getting married. After the do, we drove off in a Skoda I had at the time. (Not just a Skoda, actually, but a *mustard* Skoda, as useless a piece of Eastern bloc pig-iron as ever carried a Silesian farmer's wife to market. When it came to going away from the hotel the battery was flat, so all the best man's work – all the balloons and the cans on strings – had to be cut off so the wedding-guests could get their carnations crumpled giving us a push. How about that for symbolism?) We stopped in Stratford on the way home, stayed at a cheap tourist hotel and went to the theatre. (*Romeo and Juliet*? Of course not; it was *The Two Noble Kinsmen*, with Love and War battling it out for the soul of man. Meanwhile, back at the hotel, a simmering row between two of my brothers ended when one gave the other a split lip.)

Whatever: the point was that we didn't go away until a year or two later, when we found ourselves in Washington with a week to spare. Where would we go? I waged a clever campaign, slyly rubbishing the opposition. We hadn't the money to have real fun in New York, it was the wrong season for New England, the Blue Ridge Mountains just weren't all that Laurel and Hardy had cracked them up to be. So – deep breath – what about Nashville? Ever since that first meeting with George I'd wanted to go to Nashville, wanted to breathe in the serene poetic air that lay at the end of C&W's Yellow Brick Road. Knowing that Music City, USA, would not be Ruby's first choice, I pitched the specifics of my case carefully, not mentioning George or the Country Music Hall of Fame or the Grand Ole Opry, but focussing instead on other attractions. What about seeing the world's only perfect Parthenon replica? What about seeing the world's only guitar-shaped museum? I don't think for a moment I had her fooled, but – as in many things – she was decent in humouring my ambitions. We got a car – a Subaru, sadly, not a pink Cadillac – and drove south.

We made leisurely progress; it's fifty-five miles an hour on the freeway, and a cheery undertaker had taken billboards all over Virginia with the message DON'T RUSH – WE CAN WAIT on them. It took a day and a half, with a night in a Holiday Inn or a Hojo in the middle, before, from an exciting song-book menu on a freeway road-sign – Memphis, St Louis, Louisville, Birmingham – we chose Nashville. I remember the excitement of the approach. In search, as I was, of trash culture, the unplanned sprawl of car dealerships and scrapyards and bungalows was not a disappointment; this was the land the country radio station was speaking of in every word of every song. Then, beyond the junk, there arose spectacularly the vivid glass-gleam of the downtown offices, the international head-quarters of banks, the record companies and, of course, the Baptist publishers. There is actually more Baptist publishing business done in Nashville than there is music business, and they shine a light over the place; at night, the Baptists' thirty-five-storey high-rise has its lights left on in the shape of a crucifix.

We checked into the Downtown Ramada, where the check-in man wore a shoelace tie and the function suite was called the Johnny Cash Room. Next morning we were out and about early, picking our way down Music Row. Barely pausing to howdy Hank Wangford, who was wandering up and down the road looking for ostrich-leather cowboy boots ('Where you from?' he said with a hopeful twang, before cursing, 'Shit, you can only be from England – nobody's heard of me here') we hit the Willie Nelson (And Family) General Store and the Ernest Tubb Record Store and the Music City Waxworks and the Cars of the Stars Museum. By the second day we had ploughed a furrow through the Hall of Fame and the Johnny Cash Exhibit (slogan: 'A museum in the truest sense of the word') and the Alabama Fan Club Store and the Barbara Mandrell Experience. We went to Opryland, the theme-park to which the guardians of Nashville's heritage, bowing to the Disneyfication of the world and the need for a theatre big enough for pay-per-view concerts, have moved the Grand Ole Opry; and we still had time for half a day out at the home-cum-theme-park of the legendary Conway Twitty. We are talking, of course, that monument to bad taste known as Twitty City.

Conway is dead now (a ruptured blood vessel did for him backstage in Branson, Missouri, sometime in 1993) but he wasn't then; not physically, anyway. Conway's was not a household name on this side of the water, but in the country world – the Nashville country world, anyway – he was a demi-god. His signature-tune was the ultraweepie 'Hello, Darlin'', which runs something, in Conway's version, like this: *What's that, darlin'? How'm I doing? Yes, I'm doing just fine – except I can't sleep, and I cry all night till da-wuwu-n . . .* The welcoming-board at Twitty City takes up the theme; I have a photo of Ruby standing underneath the words H ELLO, DARLIN', and I can't look at it now without Conway's voice rising in the background, finishing the stanza with his anguished, sub-George Jones honky-tonk twang: *What I'm trying to say is I love you and need you/ and I'm sorry that I did you wra-wuwu-ng . . .*

Inside Conway's city we are treated to a cinefilm narrated by a cartoon chick called the Twitty Bird. We're invited, it says, not only to Conway's own mansion, but to the four replica mansions he has built in the grounds for his children and his mother; and, of course, the replica mansion-kennel he has built for his dog. Conway is not present today, but to enhance our enjoyment, we're shown a film of Conway flesh-squeezing other visitors on the festival known in some obscure corners of the globe as Christmas but known here as Twismas. (I am not making this up; from all his many albums, Conway's favourite was 'Merry Twismas'.) In the film, Conway emerges dressed in a red suit and white whiskers. He jumps out of his sleigh and, with the flick of a switch, lights 25,000 lamps, and he turns to the camera to tell us that he loves all his fans and that we mean the world to him.

Inside the mansion, a miniature sound-and-light show enacts the C&W soap opera that is Conway's life. As far as I can see – it's very small, the *son et lumière* set, and a coachload of bearded women is blocking my view – Conway is born next to a barbed-wire fence in Mississippi, learns his first music lying in a ditch next to the hot-gospelling Baptist church and is saved from a racial identity crisis by his mother, Velma, who sings bits and pieces from a whiter tradition under an old oak tree. The this 'n' that of his childhood becomes the rock 'n' roll of his youth and the C'n'W of his mature years; he makes records, makes it big, makes millions. (Two interesting facts: (1) Conway had a lime-green 1961 Thunderbird, registration M R T, which never left his driveway; (2) Conway got more gold discs than Elvis and the Beatles *put together*.) But Conway's real assets are, of course, his fans; or so he says as he invites us to the gifte shoppe where, besides the *Hello, Darlin'* T-shirt, we assets can pick up kitchen prayer-bells with Conway's mug-shot on them or, at $14.95, a tome entitled *Are You Related to Conway?*, which contains an exhaustive list of 4,700 members of the Twitty family. I searched it high and low, as you can imagine, and left cursing my pitifully Twitty-free genealogical heritage.

Suddenly – in writing this – I notice that Ruby has disappeared altogether beneath the weight of the crap that the Twitty Bird was dropping from the sky; and to be truthful, I can't remember where she was at this moment. I don't remember her following me around; she may have drifted off in the direction of the tea-bar, or the toilets, or simply to find a replica mansion big enough for her to throw herself off successfully. I do remember *some* moments of togetherness from the trip. I remember us sitting in a Broadway bar listening to a grizzly Waylon-alike singing about how he was the only hell his mama ever raised, and I remember a fun night in the Bluebird Café, a Nashville hangout for serious country musicians, where we enjoyed sets by six stunningly brilliant open-mike hopefuls and laughed at a desperate, handsome musician chatting up a desperate, beautiful singer with the line 'Honey – if I felt as good as you look, I'd be dancing.' But mainly I remember Ruby when we moved on to Memphis. Not so much at Graceland, for Elvis was a country boy; but she danced in the blues clubs on Beale Street with the abandon of an escaped prisoner. To my shame, I don't remember her existing in Nashville at all.

Why not? Where was she? And, more to the point, where was

I? Where was I, when she was dreaming of a husband who would spend some time with her? In the town she didn't want to visit, was I compensating her? Of course not; I was *collecting* in that oh-so-male way; collecting bargains from the record-bins, collecting giftes from the gifte shoppe, collecting gags and yarns to take back for my mates, collecting (God help me) international newspapers so that I could get the Scottish football scores. I certainly wasn't with her in any spiritual way. Yet when push came to shove, and the 'Goodbye, Darlin'' moment arrived five years later, I would spout endlessly about how I loved her and was faithful to her and wanted to be with her. But then, when I was with her, just the two of us, all alone, was I with her? No – I left her brooding as I made for the Hank Williams (And Family) General Store to pick up a statuette of Hank which doubled as a whisky decanter (the cork cunningly disguised in Hank's sky-blue stetson) and as a music-box which plays 'Your Cheatin' Heart'. Needless to say it was a long time before I realized that my heart, as well as hers, had done its share of cheating.

Maybe this is all just cheap symbolism now; I don't know. The terrible thing is that at the time of my marriage I was clear and purposeful, given what, as a half-articulate, half-formed twentysomething – as a half-articulate, half-formed twenty-something man – I knew about life and love. Some people's relationships are born of passion and find a passion to carry them into marriage and beyond. Those of us who find themselves in a relationship without that pure serene find other ways to bolster what we do. I felt at the time I married that Ruby and I had been through a lot together; that our balance of wrongs and rights was just about equalized; that in the marriage I could be stable and affectionate and clever and faithful and offer our children-to-be a solid and non-tempestuous home. I was a victim of the terrible myth that, since passion can't survive, you should get on and marry without it; that friends are all-important, that the crucial thing is to feel respect and to feel free enough to get on with burrowing in the record-bins. It's something that afflicts so many people who marry in their twenties; and it comes to afflict them again when they separate in their thirties, when passion strikes one or other and blows all the cobwebs of common sense away.

I'll never get out of this world alive . . .

That Hank statue haunted me all through my thirtieth year, sitting on the mantelpiece. In spite of having been hand-luggage mollycoddled through Customs at Gatwick, it started to fall to bits. First of all, the cork broke off the underside of the hat, making it worse than useless as a novelty drink-serving utensil; then it fell and the fretboard of the china guitar – disappointingly hollow – snapped right off. It began to feel fated. I took to looking morbidly at the inscription – 'Hank Williams, 1923–53' – and began to fear that, like Hank, I would never make thirty.

Hank Williams is the Keats of C&W in the sense that he had to achieve young because his youth was pretty much all he had. And achieve he did: by the time he was twenty-nine, he had set in hard vinyl a series of recordings which dragged hillbilly music out of the folksy foothills it had occupied since philanthropic folklorists from the Smithsonian in Washington had first collected specimens of it on wax impressions. Hank took country music and filled it full of serious melancholy and gave it a plain, hurtin' meaning that spoke to his audience of real life. It spoke to me, too. It was discovering Hank that meant that, by the age of twenty-nine, and still married, I had stopped 'collecting' C&W and had become something like a serious listener. By then the note of pain and anguish in Hank's 'Alone and Forsaken' was more important to me than the note of ludicrousness in 'My Son Calls Another Man Daddy'; by then I had discovered that for every C&W Twitty Bird there are a hundred C&W Bluebirds.

I had to suffer some ridicule for this, and not just from Ruby.

13

Because the great era of rock and pop coincided with some truly terrible years for C&W, a confession of allegiance to the pedal steel, amongst my friends anyway, would have ranked somewhere in a list of sins between confessing parricide and expressing a liking for Paul McCartney and Wings. The reason for this prejudice is simple. In the late 1950s and early 1960s the Nashville establishment, its eyes full of dollar-signs, began searching for ways to make country cross over and raid the rich pickings of the pop charts. Hank was lucky to die when he died, because, come the sixties, hillbilly Hanks and singing cowboys were no longer in demand. Country went straight to the Middle of the Road. Out went the pedal steel, in came the string orchestra. Out went the thumping fingerpick of the acoustic guitar, in came the rough-edge-softening vocal choruses. Out went the agonized plainsong of the likes of Hank, in came ballads and tear-jerkers. Out went taste, in came the bland schmaltz of the Nashville Sound; and in came the anti-C&W prejudices of my glam-rock-raised generation. Nashville sold its soul and bought a monster. Several monsters, actually; because in the seventies the Nashville Sound gave way to the even worse Countrypolitan Sound, which brought you Dolly Parton and her pneumatic pap.

But reach back to Hank across those lost decades and you hear a true country voice. Hank's themes are the great country themes – heartbreak, the road, the bottle, work, money, death – and the great country themes are the great themes of life. His songs are the classics of these themes: 'Your Cheatin' Heart', 'Mansion on the Hill', 'I'm So Lonesome I Could Cry', 'Take These Chains From My Heart', 'Lovesick Blues', 'The Lost Highway'. They are songs which are perfect in their plainness; they're rarely more than a couple of verses and a couple of minutes long; they're rough, ready and, in their regular, rhythmic beat, Homerically memorable. They're clever in their hook-lines, straightforward in their execution. They're songs of the south, but they're also songs of the universe: 'Hank provided,' says his biographer Colin Escott, 'a soundtrack for other people's lives.'

Hank had the classic country childhood I never had. First and foremost he was christened with a silly name, Hiram, by parents (Elonzo Hubble and Jessie Lillybelle Skipper) with even sillier names. His family trundled from double-pen log-house to lumber-yard boxcar to wood-and-iron shack until his father ran off, taking his Jew's harp with him, and leaving young Hiram's early musical grounding in the hands of his mother, who played organ for the Baptists. Late in life, though knowing himself to be 'a fornicator and a drunk', he would slip hymns into his beer-joint concert routines, though as a young man he developed singing cowboy fantasies watching westerns at his local Alabama flea-pit and began to dream of the lost highway that would take him to Nashville. Like Messrs Snow, Locklin and Penny, he changed his forename to Hank in the interests of hillbillity; he acquired a pea-green shirt and a pair of tooled boots; and he was soon sharing the stage with fellow-cowboy crooners. (His earliest act involved sharing the stage with a fellow-artiste who couldn't sing but who could remove a tab-end from someone's mouth with a bull-whip.) And all might have gone well, but for the fact that he met and married a woman called Audrey, a feisty, sharp-tongued, remarkably beautiful woman with a beady, ambitious eye and an icy-blue heart.

Suddenly Hank knew what pain was. His music prospered, but his life suffered; his heartache inspired, in turn, great songs and great benders. Within a few months of marrying, in 1945, he was being treated for alcoholism. A high-profile resident gig at the 31 Club in Montgomery went south when he arrived for work a little late – three days late, to be exact. He kept disappearing on binges, and pretty soon she stopped looking for him. When Audrey divorced him for the first time, in that same year, he dried out completely. He got on a radio show called the *Louisiana Hayride*, played and recorded 'Lovesick Blues' and lit a touch-paper under his career. For a brief period, it was all success; with a band featuring a man resplendently called Hillous Butrum, he issued 'You're Gonna Change (Or I'm Gonna

Leave)' and the classic 'I'm Throwing Rice (at the Girl I Love)', and the Grand Ole Opry, finally believing he could be trusted to show up now and again, signed him up at last. Even when Audrey came back, he was okay for a bit. He went on a tour of USAF bases in Europe and returned in triumph, his sales high, his veins clear, his mind set on career fulfilment . . . and immediately went on a massive bender in Dayton, Ohio.

Maybe Hank just drank because he drank; but Audrey was hardly a sympathetic helpmate, hurling tea-glasses at him when he stumbled home one night, taking an ice-pick to the tyres of his pride-and-joy Packard when he drove waywardly home another. Her rage was matched only by her acquisitiveness. He needed a Cadillac sedan to tour the country in, so she bought herself a Cadillac convertible to tour the town in. As the years go by Hank's songs, always whiny and pained – 'I'll Never Get Out of This World Alive' just about sums up his bluesy lamentation – become more poignant and more emotionally achy as they become informed by experience. 'The warmest Audrey ever got,' a Nashville figure once famously said, 'was thawing.' Once, she refused to take Hank in when a band member brought him home drunk at 5 a.m.; she insisted he be delivered to the sanatorium. At 9 a.m. she rang the same band member to ask why the tour takings hadn't been delivered. Later, finding herself pregnant, she took off to the hospital and had an abortion without telling him. Later that night he wrote 'Cold, Cold Heart'; out of a life, a classic was born.

Hank began to appear on stage drunk, and would heckle the crowd relentlessly – witty stuff like *We got a surprise for you . . . after the show we're gonna git your momma and your daddy up here and we're gonna marry them*. Record companies and promoters started to assign him minders to keep him straight for the shows; it made little difference. In 1952 the Opry ran out of patience and sacked him. Yet what's striking is that throughout the last year-and-a-half of his life he recorded sets of remarkable potency. In August '52, for instance, just after his sacking, he got pissed, but then he got focussed; he sat in the studio the next day, hungover and bruised, and, in a couple of hours, put down 'The Lonesomest Time of the Day' and 'Take These Chains From My Heart' and, supremely and definitively, 'Your Cheatin' Heart'. ('Cheating hearts,' says Escott, 'are to country music what the blues in B-flat is to jazz.') Hank then stumbled from the recording studio into the daylight, and got too drunk (by now he'd been divorced from Audrey a second time, and married Billie instead) to go on honeymoon.

He did go, however, on his last journey, its detail packed with the poetry of loss. Finding himself blacked out by many promoters and needing maintenance money, he was having to travel further and further for gigs, even if they were of the gym and church-hall sort he thought he'd left back in Alabama. Though crippled by back pain and alcohol, he accepted a gig in Canton, Ohio, in the deep midwinter. Charles Carr, a student seeking fees for the next semester, was employed to drive; but what Carr didn't know was that for some time Hank had been imbibing a lethal bit of pseudopharmacy known as chloral hydrate, a powerful sedative once famously used to put down an escaped leopard. Mixed with alcohol it was likely to prove fatal, as Dante Gabriel Rossetti, another tortured poet, had found out to his cost in 1882. And Hank felt doomed; he told Billie, before he left, that 'Every time I close my eyes I see Jesus coming down the road . . . I've got things to straighten out with the man.'

The journey was awful; icy for the driver, back-pained for Hank. They tried to stop and fly, but the flights were full and the weather too bad; so they stopped for some medicine, some morphine, which Hank threw into his stomach along with the chloral hydrate. The last Carr saw of him, he was sipping a beer in the back, utterly silent, washed-out. Carr, exhausted himself, nearly swerved off the road and hit a policeman, and was arrested; but he refused to let the judge wake Williams, taking the rap himself instead; and so the probability arises that when, at seven the next morning, he did finally try to wake Hank, he'd been dead some time, maybe all night, his soul gone, his body alone and forsaken as he made for another small-town gig for the bit-money that was a pittance compared to what he was once worth. I like to think he died at midnight.

Well; it's only a biography. But it informs: real life makes real songs, and love isn't silly at all. If there's a poetry to be found in C&W, you'll find it in Hank, however patched up his life was; Hank was more than a two-bit hillbilly. Later – years later, when the shit had well and truly hit the fan – Ruby came round to discuss the dissolution of our property. We made lists and found clever formulas – 'domestic', 'valuable', 'personal', 'sentimental' – and went through that whole, grudging process; pretending to want that to get this, staking sentimental claims to things that were never yours in the first place. Throughout the whole process Hank, minus a cork and with his guitar superglued, sat serenely, undisputedly mine, rising above the whole process like a sky-blue angel. When she'd gone, I wound up the music-box and the tinkles of 'Your Cheatin' Heart' echoed in the big space against the wall where the sofa had been.

I guess I should have known that cowboys and veggieburgers don't go . . .

One or two other things about these journeys, before they start.

Firstly, don't expect dazzling geographical pyrotechnics. After Ruby left, I took principal charge of our little ones, then aged four and six. The time spent on these journeys was conjured out of the tiny top-hat of freedom afforded to any practitioner of the magic art of single parenthood, and it wasn't always easy to get away. Secondly, prepare for the appearance of a large cast of cowboys. For although these journeys happen exclusively within the British Isles, they feature a large number of people who call country music Country and Western; whose imaginations are stalked by John Wayne and Clint Eastwood, and who have wardrobes packed to the gills with Wild West wear; people who can make an ordinary landscape look very strange indeed.

I didn't know these people existed in such numbers until I chanced on the Americana, a festival held, that year, at a grimy Midlands motor-bike race-track. I was only there by accident, really, a refugee from a moment of emotional fallout. On the first Saturday after she left, Ruby came round to pick up the children for her first contact visit. We got to arguing about something or other, as divorcers do, and for some reason vaguely connected to a sub-issue relevant to some important point or other I agreed to vacate the house for the weekend. Homeless, I rang a few friends; no answer. Determined not to be a hapless victim of solitude, I ended up scouring the newspaper for somewhere to go and stay over in the camper that had recently turned from being ours into being mine. And I saw that a great C&W hero of mine, an Austin singer named Jimmie Dale Gilmore, was playing the Americana that very day, so I drove for three hours through the madness of the midsummer M1 and the weary blear of all the bad things Ruby had told me I was and the good things she'd told me I wasn't, paid my ten quid and went in.

How was I to know, at that stage, that I was stumbling on one of the big events in the British C&W calendar? And how was I to know that British C&W-ers put their Nashville counterparts to shame? For while Nashville was pretty much a cowboy-free zone, Donington Park was crawling with cowboys. Not just cowboys, either. There were cowmen, bearded types who stood around in huddles in ankle-length *Unforgiven* raincoats; there were cow-women, dressed in stetsons and waistcoats and pointed boots or, more commonly, in the full-length red taffeta of saloon-girls; there were cow-children, in Milky Bar Kid pork-pie stetsons with white tassels. A barrowload of other weird visions arose as the day went on. I sat on the grass, listening to the Cadillac Cowboys, beside a Mexican paesano wearing a woolly waistcoat and sombrero; I waited in the beer-tent queue behind a lank-haired, flintlock-toting grey-coated runaway from the battlefield of Shenandoah; I queued for the portaloo behind a quack doctor, eminently feasible in top-hat and tails. And all this against an irredeemably British, comprehensively tawdry landscape – the long, flat, pebbledashed bits of pit-stop architecture that made up the clutch of buildings inside the motor-bike race-track (you got there by crossing a bridge in the shape of half a Dunlop tyre).

They weren't the only Yankee wannabes on show; there were Easy Riders, and Dukes of Hazzard, and good old boys, and good honest Joes, and each had a vehicle to prove it. They came cruising round the circuit in blocks: there was a host of Harleys, a plethora of pick-ups, a phalanx of Fords, a welter of Winnebagos. But even though there were a thousand romantic visions on offer – a beautiful woman rode pillion to her muscular man, connected to him only by two fingers gripping the brim of his hat – it was the cowboys that held me. They seemed jollier, richer, less likely to be illusory. The cowboys didn't, like the bikers, dismount to reveal that their bony beauty was only G-force; that, off-seat, at zero miles per hour, they were flabby and forty. And when the evening came, while the cowboys took their bottles and their partners and headed for Jimmie Dale, the bikers and the car-drivers prowled the service roads dissatisfiedly, their drivers fruitlessly cruising in search of the perfect American Saturday night there in the flatlands of Notts.

That night I felt my new solitude grip my innards in a way that none of the machinations of separation had done; this was the state beyond separation, the lost and lonely land of Interim. The girl at the Viennese Grill was wholesome and lovely and picked me out and made time to talk to me. 'I suppose I should have known,' she said, 'that cowboys and veggieburgers don't go.' But though I managed to josh that it sounded like a country song, and to promise I'd write one for her, I never went back; she was too lovely for someone in my state. Then, as Jimmie Dale moaned his way through his heartbreak set, I sat along from two nursie-looking blonde girls and smoked fag for fag with them, and sang along word for word with them to 'I'm So Lonesome I Could Cry' and 'I Still Miss Someone'; but at the end watched them get up and disappear, unchatted to by a me too worried to approach them with that boring and terrifying line, *My wife's just left me, can I be your friend?*

Before I went home, I took a last look round at the cowboy couples sitting snuggling into the night, with their low-slung deck-chairs and their *My Baby Loves Me Just Like I Am* T-shirts; and I felt questions bubbling up, felt these journeys coming on. I went home, made plans, and set off on my own immediately. Well – not quite immediately. As I say, it wasn't always easy. Ruby, just as I did, had to work sometimes; and Ruby, just as I was, was resentful and uncooperative sometimes; and Ruby sometimes had emotional crises which sometimes involved her being so overcome by love for her lost children that she could not bring herself to see them. And what with her lover being a tad overcome himself sometimes (jealous of the man he had just cuckolded, according to Ruby's later analysis), arrangements had a tendency to complicate themselves. It's a weird world, all right, that fantasy place where men dress up in stetsons and sheriff badges; but the real world runs it a pretty close second.

CHAPTER ONE

Heartaches by the Number, Troubles by the Score

'She Got the Rhythm, I Got the Blues'

Where else to start such a journey but as far west as possible?

St Columb Major, the place is called. It's a small Cornish village, and there's a cowboy café in the countryside nearby, where a solo singer called Steve Caler who's just emerged from a blue Ford Escort is singing losing songs. After the patter ('I'll do any request for a fiver or a shot of Jack Daniels, straight up') he opens with an *I lost my girl, I lost my truck, I lost my money* routine, a cover of a cover of a cover of a song by God knows who. When I go up to the bar, the grill chef, Robert, is reading a report in the paper, and he shows me; a Fatal Accident Enquiry is enquiring into the fatal accident that befell a gun-toting cowboy who, the Christmas before, had appeared on the streets at midnight brandishing a six-shooter and been shot down by the latter-day marshals of an armed response squad.

Robert's interested, because he was at one time a member of the club the cowboy drank in, 'Just one of the places I've stopped along the way,' he says. He wipes the cooking oil off his hands and comes out to have an envious look at my camper. 'Yeah – I was married, up there in Yorkshire,' he says, having a right good peer through the window. 'All ready to settle. Is that a stove? – nice. But it all went wrong.' Something in his eye makes him look happy on the road, and for a moment I imagine him wandering on purpose, the next of kin to the wayward wind.

But I've got it wrong; he's an involuntary wanderer. 'It was okay for a while. The birth was fine, the mother was fine, I was fine, happy. Then, a week later, my wife took a depression. She rejected me and the baby, just like that – overnight, like.' The details emerge without angst; he's in and looking at the sink, the stove, the storage cupboards. 'The marriage lasted just six weeks after the birth,' he says. 'She was screaming, practically homicidal. We all sat down together, her family and me, and we agreed, for everyone's good I'd go, and stay away.' His face doesn't flicker, but something in his expression says that he's killed himself with kindness; and the wayward wind did claim him, after that.

I pull the door shut and we go back in and sit down; he brings tea, milk and sugar on a tray; he lights a cigarette. 'So then I moved down here, worked for a bit, got married a second time, ended up working on the oil-rigs, out in the North Sea.' He smiles. 'Two weeks on, two weeks off, two weeks on, two weeks off.' Maybe it was that dead part of himself – the part killed with kindness – that made him cruel, but he reached the point where the two weeks on didn't seem long enough. 'You get to the time you're waiting for the helicopter to come in and you find yourself hoping for fog – that's when you know that it's time to clear out.' Another girl, another truck, another wad of money lost on the way along the lonely road; and, on cue, the crooner completes his girl, truck, money chorus: *I lost my mind somewhere along the way.*

But Robert seems a happy man, sitting there; a broad smile, a philosophical air, a clear picture of how things have panned out. He wonders about his lost child, but not too often. He works his days making burgers and fried eggs for fellow-cowboys and helping to run a Wild West theme-park, where he's made his summer bed in one of the replica buildings; he sleeps, in fact, in the jail. Now, thirteen years after his walkout, he makes his way home and finds everything is just where he left it, and says it makes him happy. (It makes me happy, too; there's something about a tidy house that satisfies the alone and forsaken.) Steve Caler is singing 'She Got the Rhythm, I Got the Blues', and then something about leaving his soul out in the rain. Robert's soul is on show, but it looks dry as a bone, looks like there's a big, thick umbrella over it. It's well wrapped-up, too, against the emotional cold, in the impeccable wool and leather blacks of his cowboy outfit, and it's my turn to be envious, as I drive off. 'I'm a cowboy who happens to be a grill chef, not a grill chef who happens to be a cowboy,' he says as a goodbye; he's settled and it's I who's moving on.

'When I dress up, I always put on these gloves – these tight leather gloves – last. And as soon as I've done that, then I see nobody – you can't feel self-conscious.' He makes it sound like being on stage, like acting, when the brightness of the lights blocks out the faces of the audience. 'I put this stuff on, and I'm a different person; it's like coming to life.'

That brought tears to my eyes . . .

Driving out to Cornwall feels like a Wild West journey as the A30 stretches out in the night. I cross the River Tamar, dividing the Cornish from the English like some miniature Rio Grande, and as I skirt Dartmoor and begin to cross the long stretch of Bodmin Moor, I just can't stop songs of the lone prairie stealing into my head. (Later, I learn that the urban Cornish actually call the Moor people Illybillies; the world is full of westerns.) The roads start to be fringed with cattle warning signs. Either I've been driving too long or there's something seriously wrong with my sexual self-esteem, for as I go on I'm convinced that the cattle are getting manlier. I am sure the cow on the first sign is hornless, but the second, third and fourth cows are depicted as increasingly protuberant in the antler department, whilst the fifth, with a nifty stroke of an adolescent's pen, has grown an ominous dangle between its back legs.

But the cowboys at the Lonesome Dove Club in Redruth don't threaten; they're sweeties. There's Phil, a nice bloke with droopy sideburns, a hillbilly hat and a pint of Double Diamond, who invites me back to his place for a five-hour screening of the whole *Lonesome Dove* series; and there's Custer, a nice longhair in checks and a waistcoat, who lectures me about Hollywood's mythologizing of the American west and shows me his gleaming grey Smith & Wesson. (I do a reasonable job of twirling it, then give it back when my arm begins to ache.) Their weapons are not left at the door of the flat prefab where the club meets, but, beneath the flags and drapes of the Texas Rangers and the Lone Star State, they are checked by Arnold, the toothless safety officer.

Up on stage there's a smoothie called Dusty Rhodes, who has a Garth Brooks black-and-white chequerboard shirt and one of those headpiece microphones that make a singer look like he works in telesales. His slick-dickery doesn't quite merge with his surroundings, for – for all the cowboy gear, for all the flags and Indian banners lining the walls – this is a classic English social club. There are longways tables fringing a bashed parquet dance-floor oddly illuminated from the lights (frosted-glass efforts in green, red and yellow) above; a bar dealing cheap pints of Foster's; and a hatch in one of the gaudy orange walls with a hidden caterer sending out sausages and crinkle-cuts on polystyrene trays for the cowboys to graze on.

Blossom and Mike nod hello; Mike adds a western handshake, a grasp of the thumb rather than the fingers. He's thin and grey and rather frail-looking, with a tic that betrays his speech every now and then; Blossom is bouncy and buxom and befrilled. They are a four-nights-a-week cowboy couple, and the names of the clubs trip off their tongues with a matter-of-fact poetry; the Lonesome Dove, yes, but also the Blues and Greys over in St Austell, the Golden Garters in Newquay, the Heavy Transport on Par Moor. Blossom is life-and-soulishly hard to pin down; as we talk she is constantly pestered by howdying cowboys and how-ing Indians, by screeching saloon-girls, even by a man dressed as a parson who hands his kid a Bible and asks him to find the Book of Revelation. Mike is more quiet, more hesitant; redundant now, he has a look in his eye that says he has less assurance than Blossom about where he stands in the world's estimation.

He's a victim of short-time working, as it turns out; after twenty-six years as a steward at a naval base, his job went when catering operations were put out to tender. He struggled in the new world of contracts and sessions, and had just got his feet under the table with some contractors when a heart attack hit him. And so he was out: and here he sits, with a pint of Coke, a stammer and twenty unwise Superkings. There is no other work, he says. 'There were tin-mines, once upon a time, but they shut down, in the sixties, seventies, eighties.' He makes it sound like a gold-rush town, only slower; the gold without the rush. 'Other people worked on the land, but the farms around here have been growing smaller for years, and of course they're all' – he struggles with his face and tongue over the start of the word – 'm-mechanized.' He had taken to redundancy badly, and found it harder work than work. 'What kind of life is that for a man?' he asks. 'Sitting in a chair all day . . .'

Blossom is earwigging, and her interest in her other conversation capsizes like a coracle; how hard can sitting in a chair all day be? You can see at a glance that she'd be happy with all the time to talk that all day could bring, but she, she says, is 'run off her feet'. She's an auxiliary nurse, and I have a vision of her lifting babies out of the maternity ward and settling them in virgin car-chairs, of waving off the new family saloons and coming home, tired, to a melancholy man. 'It's like having a baby around the house,' she says. 'I have to work all day,' she says, 'then I cook, I clean, I wash up.' Her smile and her kiss for another friend, who brings over a basket of fruit, a raffle prize, say that it's not what she expected from life.

Yet heart attacks are nothing new to her. Her first husband, a draughtsman, dropped dead at the wheel of his car when he was in his forties. He had followed the money to Bedfordshire and she had followed him from her Cornwall home; and when he popped his clogs, just like that, she obeyed his dying wish that she should go home. But whatever kind of control the draughtsman hoped to establish with his beyond-the-grave contract, he hadn't counted on Mike, the St Austell cowboy, riding in and sweeping her off her newly widowed feet. Now, on cue, he goes off to get holstered up for the half-time shootout. Blossom, sipping her shandy, watches him go, and we talk about music for a while. She doesn't like Loretta Lynn or Tammy Wynette or any of the saints in the hard-life-for-a-woman litany; she likes Hank Williams and Johnny Cash, and, bizarrely, 'John Wayne — I like John Wayne. I've four pictures of John Wayne at home. Two in the bedroom, two in the sitting-room . . .' One, presumably, hanging above the chair where Mike sits all day.

Jolly for a bit, we talk about my children. Perhaps it's my vision of her at work, carrying babies to cars; perhaps it's the fact that fifteen women in this room tonight have behaved as if they might be her daughter; but I'm surprised when she says she has none of her own. In fact, worse: 'I had twins,' she says, 'but I lost them. Back in Bedfordshire.' Her eyes go hollow. Dusty is hitting the sombre notes of 'The Speed of the Sound of Loneliness', and the lurid basket of fruit from the raffle, the one that one of her 'daughters' has pried into to pinch a Snow White apple, suddenly looks like the sort of Interflora thing you only buy to take to a hospital. 'I saw a programme the other day,' she says, for the first time not looking at me as she talks, 'about those twins you get that are joined at the neck.' She has to look at me for a moment, to show just where; but it is only a moment before her face dips: 'That brought tears to my eyes, it did. Tears to my eyes.' And for once she doesn't disappear off to say hello to anyone, but sits in her chair, and lights a cigarette, and looks over at the dance-floor.

The line-dancers she's watching are deep into a one-step-forward, two-steps-back routine; one of them, fattish and speccy, smiles at me as if I'm carrying a video camera; Dusty sings the line about being out there running just to be on the run. Mike returns, looks at Blossom's face and gives me a little reproachful look, as if he knows what heavy treading I've been doing; that it will be he and his dicky heart who have to pick up the pieces, who'll have to give therapy from the John Wayne chair. He shows me his gun. 'They're safe in the right hands,' he says, unmenacingly, 'but in the wrong hands, they're lethal weapons.' He looks at my hands as if they're the wrong hands, reclaims his weapon and leaves me standing alone at the bar.

'A Good Year for the Roses'

I'm discreet on these travels; even way out in Cornwall I have no hat, no waistcoat, no holster; just the brown boots, my faithful accessory, primly and privily tucked away under my Levis. But there are times when I wish to be dressed up, protected, like Robert clearly is, like, for all I know, Phil and Custer might be.

As the long summer of pain and rationalization and heavy smoking ends with Ruby's final departure, I have a rush of glad-she's-gone euphoria as the stress of all the late-night discussion and analysis ends. But beyond that, as a pattern to things develops and the adrenalin that change has created disperses, comes a period of pain and isolation which is difficult to endure. Part of it is a simple loneliness, a longing. Part of it is a fearful wonder about where and what one is and where one is going. And part of it is the need that all the trashed-on have, to somehow take what has happened and prove something to the trasher; to somehow, even as one loses, win; to keep talking, even if, after all the pointless reiteration, *there's so little left to say we haven't said* . . .

It helps to have stayed in the house, of course, to not have to have moved; yet it would help not to have to stay in the house, not to have to walk into the rooms we shared, not to have to trip over the love she left behind. I listen to George a lot, as he croons about the sight of cigarettes left cold in the ashtray and the lip-rim on a cup of coffee which is poured and never drunk:

> *Well at least you thought you wanted them,*
> *That's so much more than I can say for me.*

And though Ruby didn't smoke, or drink coffee particularly, there are empty drawers in the house, and spaces on the book-shelf; there are things that were there and now aren't, and each discovery has the kung-fu fighting skill to catch you in the emotional stomach.

Of course it helps not to have to worry about what your rival in love has to offer; gazed at through my eyes (and through my spectacles, which are as malice-shaded as Ruby's are rose-tinted), the Greek is an easy target for my wicked tongue. One night, as we argue on the phone (for some reason he insists on calling me from time to time), I rashly say that I think he looks like a penis. I develop the comparison in unflattering terms, making sure that the sort of penis I compare him to is not the long and elegant sort that I believe myself to possess; the sort I am thinking of, I say, is squat and bulbous and has a satyr-like appearance. (I put the phone down without realizing that I have strayed into insecurities of his; he is unmanned for quite a time afterwards, as if I'd taken a cleaver rather than mere words to his vital organs.) Yet even when you despise your rival, you still envy the sense of direction that his love brings, and you fall into wondering whether you'll ever be loved again. You start to consider your waistline and your shyness. You count the cost of being with children but without money. You remember every sexual failure from adolescence to the present day, especially those with the she-just-departed. Soon you're planning all sorts of stupid changes in your life, in the hope that you'll find someone or something to cling on to.

While a million thoughts go racing through my mind
I find I haven't said a word . . .

And it helps to be keeping the children, of course; not to be banished into that Waste Land of Saturdays at the zoo, but to have the assurance that, above all, you will be the central figure in their lives; to think that you, as a male figure, will form them, rather than some slaphead their mother has taken up with. But they hold you, too; you feel burdened by the strain of their strain, as they talk to you about baby animals being separated from their parents, as they offer to do without pocket-money if that will help; as, having sussed out the situation, having deduced at last that a flat is not the same as a hotel, they begin to tease each other with hissed lines about how Mummy is never coming home. And they do do these things; all the *Kramer versus Kramer* clichés are true, and you feel you can't leave them for a moment or they'll fall into a suicidal abyss, even though they're small enough to sort their own heads out. You suffer with them; and, like some emotional surgeon handling a new grafting process, you etch your pain on them.

And, believe it or not, the house we shared together does have a rose-garden out the front; the roses were the pride and joy of the man who owned it before and, unkempt, they do, they really do have their best-ever summer and autumn in this desolate year.

What a good year for the roses, many blooms still linger
there
The lawn could stand another mowing, funny – I don't even
care.
As you turn to walk away, as the door behind you closes
The only thing I have to say is, 'It's been a good year for the
roses'.

If you're not separated these days then you're on your own . . .

Christmas is on a Monday this year so the Sunday papers, with all that space to fill, are full of Crisis at Christmas stories; stories of homeless shelters opening up, stories of single mothers (mainly) struggling to put together a normal Christmas on Income Support and enduring the galling sight of their long-gone spouses brazenly turning up in M-reg cars and unloading barrowloads of goodies for their long-neglected children. What the children miss, an article says, is what they remember from the past – dressing the tree with Mum and Dad together. What the single parent misses is buying the present for that special person, receiving the special thing back; those aching moments which memory makes worse by placing them here, in a season.

My children are with Ruby for Christmas, so I play a few games with myself, secretly enjoying the idea of a day's self-pitying solitude. I go out on Christmas Eve and buy myself a meal for one and, anything but pathetically, the smallest box of Quality Street on the shelves; no family-size tin for me. I lie on the floor of the lounge and watch the soaps. The Yuletide storylines suggest anything but a misty-eyed, mythical well-spring of happiness. On *Brookside* there's an AIDS test and a compulsive gambler bringing ruin to her family, and on *EastEnders* Arthur's in prison and someone else is harassed by an estranged spouse. Yet there is pain; I shop for the children with joy, but run out of steam and energy when it comes to finding anything for anyone else, and hear all the time in my mind the Merle Haggard song about shopping for dresses with no one to wear them.

I go for a swim in the end, late on Christmas Eve. The pool, one of those big glassy jobs, is bright on the outside and quiet on the inside. Swimming is nice when you feel soiled; it's something about immersion, something about having a tidy body to go with a tidy house. But as I pass through the lobby I see my children through the glass wall of the swimming-pool and watch them messing about with Ruby and the Greek; I cannot hear their voices, and when I knock on the glass they can't hear me. As 'My Son Calls Another Man Daddy' experiences go, it's a slight one, and I'm buttressed by the knowledge that most of the year it's not like this; the children live with me, I have not been in prison or away or out of touch. Yet it's a hard one, and by seven on Christmas Eve I'm anticipating the hour I'll have with them on Christmas Day in a way I'd never imagined. The house is quiet, and in next door's lounge the grandchildren are making a whole heap of jolly-sounding noise.

It's less of a white than a tawdrily psychedelic Christmas at the Wagon Wheel Club in Reading. The Civil Service sports club pavilion where it meets is bedecked from ceiling to floor with red and blue tinsel which reflects in an ungainly way off the disco globe; this could be any Christmas party from ballroom to disco, but as it happens it's country. The singer is Pete Palmer, a brown-toothed man in reactolites working five nights a week and with a line in growing-old patter that's well practised; the jokes are as long in the tooth as he is. *This is a song about a well-known DIY chain. Yes, it's God Bless Texas . . .*

June and Dave and their friend Esme call me over to their table. June is a sixty-year-old recently retired school cook. She's struggling; she's developing flu and bronchitis, she's had a fall, she has broken a hip, she has a bruise on her face and she is supporting herself in a clearly pained way. She's in the lemon-yellow and frilly sort of frock that's the fave rave of C&W women. Dave, sometime factory worker, now a cleaner of offices and, lately, 'operative' at the new Legoland in Windsor, cuts a jauntier figure. He has a blue shirt with an appliqué bald eagle on the back and little motif wing-tips on the collar. He has narrow jeans, though he's wearing a plain pair of Hush Puppies ('my dancing shoes') rather than boots. In deference to June's condition he's not prowling the floor tonight, though he obviously loves it and his eyes drift twinkily, from time to time, to the couples spinning round the floor. June meanwhile looks like she couldn't twinkle tonight if she was a whole galaxy of little stars.

They have matching jackets from a western dance club they're members of. The jackets are white blousons, American-styled, with *Keep It Country* emblazoned on the back. On the front there's the Buffalo Club motif and beneath the badge are their pet names. June's is Blossom, which is hardly a surprise for a yellow rose of Texas; Dave's, more surprisingly, is Petal. It comes from a time when he worked as a security guard at night and used to pass the time by calling in to radio quizzes and phone-ins. Obviously, when on company time – not to mention on the company phone – he didn't use his own name. He'd phone in and call himself Petal; she, listening at home while he worked the graveyard shift, would ring in with her request for a country number as soon as she heard his message.

It's a radio romance, theirs. Like so many C&W couples, they've found love wonderful the second time around. June was divorced while in her forties and won't say much about her first husband that can't be said in a smiley sneer. After Dave's first wife died of cancer when he, too, was in his forties, he was on the lookout for a new partner; perhaps that should be spelt western-style, since they have named their house Pardners' Paradise. In his first period of searching Dave went ballroom dancing, but it was all wrong; even when he had got over the silent inward scream of bereavement which he heard at the dance-hall door every night, he still had to deal with the fact that the partnership interests of the ballroom women he met were confined to the dance-floor. Finally he got out his tape-recorder – he can't read or write, he says, in answer to my raised eyebrow – and taped a message – 'Country fan seeks dancing partner', or whatever. His sister-in-law typed it up for him and they sent it in to a local radio station. The first person who replied was June. 'I like him,' was her first reaction; her second, according to Dave, 'Is he black?' The answer being negative, they had got together; eight years, but who's counting?

'The secret is – give and take,' he says. Who does the giving and who does the taking? He laughs, kindly, then lists a number of duties that they divide. Some are at home, but the one he keeps repeating is how they behave on the road; he drives, she navigates. From each according to his means; illiterate, he needs her to read the map. Later, when it's time to go, she writes crystal-clear directions for us to follow, like someone who's used to doing the writing. And, in pain, she tells me what she's been doing tonight; she entertains herself at country concerts by writing poems as she watches. She's scribbling while I'm talking to Dave, though she's not forthcoming – 'Not till it's finished.' When she starts to cough Dave, the man who can't write, slaps her about fifty times on the back. 'Give and take,' he says with a laugh, as her eyes go goggly, and she continues to write a poem that he will never read.

Esme, who's listened, then begins to talk. For her it's an especially hard Christmas; her husband died just a year ago. 'He died on New Year's Eve but he was on a ventilator from Christmas Eve, so I always say he died then.' She is a clear-faced, pleasant woman who talks without bitterness; yet what she has to say comes out in a rush and what's in it is not easy. Her husband, Jim, was a Glaswegian, a fervent Rangers supporter, but, Reading-ized, happy enough to marry off his daughter to an Irishman called Dermot Murphy. He worked in refrigeration in Glasgow, then came to Portsmouth for National Service where Esme met him thirty-seven years ago; though unable to work out a word he was saying, she was overcome by his geniality, and she conjures up a romantic image – a traveller, a native, a smile of welcome, a smile of love.

In Reading Jim took a job as a builder, then, working for himself, as a roofer. He was a bright man, a breezy man, Esme says – 'Always the first on the dance-floor, he was, never a touch of embarrassment' – but at fifty-nine had had an accident with bitumen and been so badly burned that he had spent two months in Stoke Mandeville. Esme and her daughters think that the burns started a reaction through his body. He had problems with different parts of himself and then, latterly and particularly, his gall-bladder. He was rushed to hospital in Reading just before that Christmas Eve, and, as his condition worsened, he was transferred to Birmingham for an operation. But it wasn't the operation that did for him; incredibly, in some ghastly *ER* or *Cardiac Arrest* scenario, Jim reacted badly to the antibiotics prescribed for him and went into the coma out of which he never emerged. Esme remembers how the doctor who came to comfort her ended up collapsing herself: 'Imagine – I had *her* – the doctor – weeping in my arms,' she says.

She doesn't know if she's entitled to compensation, but even if she was it would be of no consolation. At fifty-nine, Jim had been cheated of his retirement; the retirement of a genial man, a family man, not someone (like Mike) for whom retirement is a pain and a comedown and an anticlimax. Esme meanwhile has been cast into a world in which she clearly keeps her chin up, while smarting at the salt water creeping up around her neck. She has not been left in financial trouble, but the house has too many rooms and she feels that she is rattling about; she has family – three daughters and grandchildren – and she recognizes that it would be worse not to have them, but daughters are not the same as a husband. She has Dave and June, who have been wonderful, bringing her out every month to the Wagon Wheel – but when she gets there she has to look at all the couples dancing, and each couple's coupleness reproaches her fate.

Pete, oblivious to any such currents, is still making jokes and doing Alan 'Hunk in the Hat' Jackson numbers, though he's twenty years too old and twenty degrees too ugly. But he's a fine singer and he does tune in to something: *Some days are diamonds*, he sings, *Some days are stones/ Sometimes the hard times/ Won't leave you alone . . .* On Christmas Eve at a year's remembrance time, hard times won't leave you alone, though the break and the raffle and the baskets of chips arrive. Esme touches my arm in a maternal sort of way and asks if I have children. I tell her I have two, but that I'm separated from my wife. 'Oh,' she says calmly, 'everyone's separated these days. Nobody stays married at all. If you're not separated these days you're on your own.'

I slip out to the toilet for a bit, and when I return – we're into the third and last segment of Pete's act – Dave has done the logical thing with his itchy feet and Esme's partnerlessness and taken her for a dance, leaving June at the table writing on her pad. (She sends me the poem later: it's personal, addressed to me, called 'Your First Visit': *Amidst good music, and applause/ We had a visit from Santa Claus./ Friendship and warm embraces/ Our family club, with happy faces.)* Dave too is quite a performer, in a flashy, Hammersmith Palais sort of a way; one of those men who slump at the table then perk up in every part of their physique when the dance-floor calls.

He's swish, swishy; he sweeps Esme round. I know what Esme's feeling, that it may be good, but it won't satisfy. To dance with your friend's wife is just to have what Dave couldn't take; that feeling that no one's talking to you, that things aren't moving forward, an endless frustration of the yearning for relationship. Pete plays that slushy number by Don Williams, 'You're My Best Friend', when Esme and Dave come back and sit down, and as if to confirm, Esme says, 'I know I'll never marry again.' I must have looked up quizzically, because she adds, 'My daughters say how can I say that already? But I know no one'll ever take the place of my Jim.' Her loyalty is her screen, her silent scream; her nobility is the device that makes her house too big and ensures that it will always be so. She, one senses, won't get some Cyrano to make her tape-recording into a message of invitation. Pete Palmer does not play any Merle Haggard tonight; neither 'If We Make It Through December', which is a shame, nor, for that matter 'Shopping for Dresses'. I wish he would, for the second stanza is an optimistic maybe; in the second stanza, the man shopping for dresses hopes that there's a lady shopping for britches, hopes that the good Lord will bring them and their wardrobes together. I smile at Esme, moved by her resolution. She looks at the hole in my jeans.

Larger than life and twice as hard . . .

Merle had his heartaches, of course, as did all the country singers who take their place in my C&W pantheon. Hank did, of course; and George, and Willie, and Johnny, and Tammy. (Maybe even Conway – who knows? Maybe he was once lonely this Twismas.) Patsy Cline was not a woman whose life ended happily, either, though one's heart goes out not so much to her as to her husband, Charlie, who was left behind after the plane carrying Patsy and Hawkshaw Hawkins and Cowboy Copas went down in a foggy swamp in 1963. Charlie's grief extended over years, it's said. He left the house just as it was – Patsy's clothes in the wardrobe, her hairspray in the bathroom – and he used the bottle to change the nature of where he lived. Drunk, he would play her records over and over again, returning, they say, again and again, to 'Faded Love' . . .

They're compelling, these star-tales; like stories of saints, they veer in and out of myth while offering up detail of pain that's anything but mythical. Patsy was married before she met Charlie, but Gerald had hightailed it by 1956; he'd come to believe, as Patsy slept away the days and sang away the nights, that the household motto should be 'All for one and one for one'. It took her only a year to get to the altar with Charlie, whom she described forthrightly as 'a hurricane in pants'; he was, she liked to say, 'larger than life and twice as hard'. Along with Charlie came her big break, 'Walking After Midnight'. In fact the record depressed her; she thought it was just a 'little ole pop song'; she wanted to country-girl yodel on the Opry, not dress up to cross over to soft rock. But Nashville dressed her up to cross over anyway, in tight hips and sequins, in gold lamé and high heels, and the throaty, bluesy, sexy edge that she gave that song carried her onwards and upwards.

Patsy is another example of how country art comes to reflect country life. 'A Church, A Courtroom and Goodbye' provided the soundtrack for her time with Gerald. When Charlie was conscripted into the military, Patsy whiled away the time he was at Fort Bragg recording 'Write Me (Care of the Blues)'. As it became clear that her early deal with an unscrupulous producer meant that she was never going to make big money, it was 'Stop the World (And Let Me Off)'. As Charlie, home again, began to believe she should be likewise, instead of out and about every night, and as, irritated, he began to drink, and he began to neglect, and he began to beat, 'That's How a Heartache Begins' was on those ruby lips. And if that's how it begins, then 'I Fall to Pieces' is how it ends.

It went something like this: she would sing nights and come home. He would get drunk and beat her up. She would blow up and have him arrested. She would phone everyone in town and tell them he was a bastard, that she was never going to let him back in. Satisfied, she would go to sleep, wake up, go down to the police station and bail him out, and the cycle would begin again. Yet no spin of the honky-tonk merry-go-round seemed to be able to drive them apart big-time; right on cue came the mansion on the hill. It was a dream-house in Goodlettsville, with heritage furnishings, a white satin *chaise longue*, a gold-sprinkled bathroom, a rug in the shape of a gold disc; and in the wardrobe there was a tiara Patsy would hold to her head as, at the mirror, she would pronounce herself Queen of Country Music.

Well – she was worth something; she was the first C&W woman to become something other than a cutesie ornament, and she paved the way for the many fine female leads of the present, for the Rebas and the Pams and the Mary-Chapins. You still can't turn her death into Hank's, even if Roger Miller searched the swamps all night; but you do go back to Charlie, sitting at home, nursing their two children and his heartbreak, and through the mist of myth you can see something there to be lamented. Because that voice – even if you know nothing about her, her version of Willie Nelson's 'Crazy' can bring you out in a cold sweat – and the thought of listening to your lover's voice, as warm as she is now cold, on record, in the dream-house, as the children cry in the nursery . . . that's a hard life, and harder than mine. Even if it is just a myth.

What's for ye won't go by ye . . .

In my youth there was a Glaswegian country singer called Sydney Devine who acquired a bit of local fame for a while. After a couple of appearances in the Radio Clyde charts (I had a pretty good impersonation at one time of the way he warbled the opening line of one of them – *I wa-aw-ndered too-woo-daaay to the hi-ills, Maggie* – he was given his own show on the station. I thought he was a truly awful singer but he was shriekingly popular in Glasgow, especially on the Daniel O'Donnell/Granny-throw-yer-knickers circuit; and he made a good living pulling in expat Scottish audiences in the States, in Canada, in New Zealand. A lefty satirical singer called Peter Nardini – the Billy Bragg of Lanarkshire – recorded a tribute to Sydney's legendary capacity to tear-jerk: *He brought tears to my eyes/ Well, he even brought tears to my kidneys/ I wish I could sing like Sydney . . .*

Sydney, I suppose, was my first C&W grounding. In what I now realize was a pretty sound parody of traditional C&W behaviour, I used to tune in to Sydney's programme. Like Hank Williams or George Jones sitting in their shacks waiting for the WSM call-sign that would announce the start of the Grand Ole Opry, I would wait with bated breath for that jingly *Radio Clyde – 261* opening, and with even bateder breath for Sydney's chirpy Ayrshire tones to sign off two hours later with those immortal words: *Put the kettle on, Shirley – I'm coming home.* I had always wondered what had become of Sydney — he was tubby and middle-aged-looking even in those days, back in the mid-seventies. Was he now a bloated cabaret artist? Was he big in Australia? Had he, like a footballer whose playing days are over, bought a pub and, when the currency of his fame had become worthless, reinflated it in his head by drinking his own joint dry?

In fact, Sydney Devine is alive and well. At the Texas Star, which meets in a Catholic club in Barrhead, a concretey outcrop to the south of Glasgow, Veronica shows me a picture, taken just the previous weekend at a C&W convention at Butlin's in Ayr, of herself posing with Sydney. He is looking just the ticket, hardly a day older, still with the same angelic chops and mid-seventies part-bobbed and blow-dried haircut. Veronica must be Sydney's age, but she looks older; a lovely, open woman in a — another — bright lemon frilly dress. She none the less looks like she might have suffered, and she has. She was married to Sam, who died of cancer a few years back, at fifty-five. He died on Hogmanay, and while Sam first-footed his way through the afterlife Veronica sat at home, middle-aged and washed-up.

Sam and his friend Vic and another man used to come to the Texas Star; they were all three English and used to hang around together. 'The Three Musketeers, we used to call them,' Veronica says. About the time Sam died, Vic was married, but tied up with another woman. He asked Veronica for her opinion but she wouldn't give it: 'It's not for me to say,' she had told him. She gives it now, however, acidly and conclusively: 'She'd had a dozen men before and she's had a dozen since,' she says. As the straight-up virtuous woman mocks the honky-tonk angel, the band strikes up with 'Don't the Girls Get Prettier at Closing Time'.

Vic's relationship with Jean trickled on for a while, and it broke up his first marriage. He looked after Sam's wife, though, while neglecting his own. Veronica: 'I had become a vegetable since Sam died; just sitting round the house, never going out, never seeing anybody.' But Vic would turn up and take her out to the Texas Star and to the other country clubs where they had all gone before, when they were still the Three Musketeers and Her. 'He wouldny take any money,' Veronica says. 'Wouldny let me pay for petrol or buy a drink or nothing. Looked after me. Never a thought for himself. So – though I missed Sam – gradually I was getting back to normal.' Vic was still seeing Jean, though that died the death when she moved on to the first of the figurative second dozen. So it was a good couple of years before Vic, at the same annual Ayr Butlin's event where Veronica had met Sydney, had asked her out. 'It was nice,' Veronica says, 'it was like friends.' She smiles a smile that's anything but wan, that radiates; her way of saying, 'Enough said.' And all she'll add, in summary, is, 'It's like they say, son – what's for ye won't go by ye.'

I leave her alone for a bit; she's totting up the admission money, counting the raffle-tickets. I watch Vic instead; he's howdying, thumb hand-shaking, laughing, being a man about the place. He's a good-looking man who, like Sydney, is probably the same age as Veronica but doesn't look it; life seems to age women more than men in these parts. He came from Hassocks in Sussex, originally, and has an odd mix of accent; the south coast rings through it, even if Glaswegian wouldnys and didnys wedge and divot their way in from time to time. He's beautifully dressed in a long, almost floor-length black gambler's coat, a frilly shirt, a waistcoat with chain. He has the long hair swept back and spilling over the collar and the droopy moustache that makes the best western look. He watches the band play 'Just Call Me Lonesome' and taps his feet in a way that says they're conclusively not playing his song.

I ask the obvious question about melancholy music and how it meshes with his less-than-melancholy manhood. 'People get this music wrong,' Vic says. 'We had a guy from the *Evening Times* here one night, and he says, "How can you stand it? How can all you C&W types listen to this suicidal music?" I said to him, "What do you mean, suicidal? You look round this room and show me one person who's suicidal. I bet you can't find one person like that." I said, "Take me. I was in a bad marriage for years . . ."' Veronica, alertly looking up from her scroogeing, says, hastily, for him: 'Listen, son. Vic's not the suicidal sort. But he says to this bloke, "I was in a bad marriage for years and it's this, it's this music, that kept me from being suicidal. It was this that kept me sane." Son, we never knew that about Vic, by the way, we never knew he was unhappy at home. All we knew was that his wife didn't like country music, that he came to the club alone and that he went home alone. We only heard about it all when he left his wife for Jean, and that was that.'

Vic leaves her to talk, to fill in the pieces. He has to run. He has the band to MC, a celebrity spot to compère, an interval shootout to organize, half-time bingo to call. Veronica shows me the roll-call for the shootout. The members participating are using their *noms de plume* – perhaps that should be *noms de fusil*. There's Silver Blade versus Wyatt Earp, Black Jack versus Boxcar, Texas Rose versus the Rodeo Kid, Lee Van Cleef versus Sneaky Pete. Down the list there's even – someone getting his Clint Eastwood wires crossed – a Dirty Harry. Completely uncrossed is Sidewinder, whose handle is by far the wittiest, because Sidewinder, although he's a huge, chunky man who looks like he could have taken a bull by the bollocks in his youth, is now confined to a wheelchair.

Vic is the Wrangler, and has a perfect record over the weeks of their shooting season. Veronica – Abilene Rose – shows me his record in the score-book, and it's a long line of perfect twos. She doesn't even look up as he takes his mark; she just says, 'Watch it – he'll get a two again.' BANG! 'The Wrangler,' the Judge calls. BANG! 'The Wrangler.' Veronica writes down another '2' beside his name. 'That's me, psychic,' she says with a laugh. She's proud as she tells me about the fact that they have a trophy, that Vic will undoubtedly win it. I watch him polish off the rest of the line-up. It seems a bit unsporting that Vic, who's something of a tyro in the western scene in this part of the world, should bother about taking the trophy when the opposition is so feeble; when up against him is a man who thinks 'Go on, make my day' is a western challenge, or a man who has chrome wheels instead of legs.

Innocent, I ask where they got the trophy from. Did someone sponsor it? 'No,' Veronica says, '*I* donated it. I set it up.' She had given it, and named it after Sam, her ex-husband, as a kind of a memorial. 'His handle was Bret Maverick – that's what he called himself, his western name – so I named it the Bret Maverick Trophy.' Suddenly it all coheres; the pieces fit, the penny drops. Sam and Vic are friends, the Porthos and Aramis of the Three Exotic Englishmen. Sam passes over to the other side, to hillbilly heaven. Vic looks after Veronica, first one way, then another. ('Nice – like friends.') Veronica remembers Sam by engraving a piece of silver with Bret Maverick, Sam's real name, the name of her husband. Vic becomes her husband and wins the Bret Maverick Trophy with perfect scores, with a long line of twos, year after year after year. And he takes it home and puts it on Veronica's sideboard, next to the picture of Bret Maverick.

As an image of something pretty much like adjustment – of dealing with trouble, with death, with broken marriages, with faithless women, with pretty much all the ills that life can bring, and coming out on top – it seems pretty much perfect. The idea of a choice – to choose between being a Mike or a Robert or a Dave or a Vic – suddenly seems open, and that's a liberating thing after months of discussion which, in retrospect, you realize would only lead in one direction; less a crossroads, more a cul-de-sac. For the moment the knowledge that, at some stage, it becomes a choice, is what Kenny Rogers would call an ace that I can keep; not to play, but to hold on to until the confusion and loss subsides – as I know it must, though I panic and react and struggle, when I'm alone in the van or the house – and life begins again.

CHAPTER TWO

Tonight the Bottle Let Me Down

It's known as a nervous breakdown...

I'm at the Lone Rock Club in Roche, and a band called Alligator Stew are playing straight, old country, the gritty pre-CMT stuff of trains and honky-tonks and broken hearts. 'They won't touch Garth Brooks with a barge-pole. They know what we like,' grins Jim, a gentle-looking pardner with a black stetson and a long train of hair hanging down over his collar. 'For me, new country isn't country. It's too much like rock.' But he rocks himself, in his own way; he leaps up to join in a line-prancing routine to Johnny Cash's 'Orange Blossom Special' which includes each dancer miming the pull of a train whistle.

Jim sits down again when things slow down, when the stomping gives way to something pedal-steely and melancholic. Jim – like everyone in this honky-tonk world, it seems – was married before he met Sylvia. Sylvia's a big, open woman, as nice as the day is long. Their daughter, beside her ('We never use babysitters – she always comes with us'), has the imitative, only-child manner of someone who spends too much time with adults, but she holds me with a ten-minute account of West Country myths which fill my dreams when I return to my van that night; the story of the saint who lived on the rock behind the club, and that of Tregeagle, who sighed windily as he penitentially tried to empty the bottomless Dozmare Pool.

We talk for a bit about what's on my mind; about children, about problems of access and contact and custody. Jim has a kid, Heidi, by his previous wife, and Heidi is the same age as Sylvia's daughter by her first marriage. When the two girls were brought together they fought, and soon Jim's ex-wife stopped bringing her up from Plymouth; so Jim stopped seeing his kid, as simple as that. Sylvia, open-faced, listens to my worries about my own situation patiently, but has a world-view – forgive and forget – which means that she doesn't really listen to the detail. She forgives Heidi for making things difficult. She forgives Jim's ex-wife for bowing to the inevitable. She forgives her own ex-husband for never being around to make things run better. 'You have to accept these things,' she says, 'start from the place where you say, it's nobody's fault.' Lo and behold: Heidi, unseen for several years and now twenty-one, had turned up of her own volition a few months before, just walked in the door. Just another 'Bedtime Story', as Tammy Wynette would call it.

But they're not all as cosy as that. Coming through the quarry-like china clay works that surround Roche I'd noticed an eerily impressive sight: a line of six or seven monstrously huge dumpers parked idle on the crest of one of the quarry waste-mountains. As it happened, I was listening to Cash on the tape-machine at the time, and he does a Guy Clark song about a man driving some sort of big rig powerful enough to push the Rockies into the sea; *Heavy Metal,* he says, *Don't Mean Rock 'n' Roll to Me.* And there they sat, power mo-chines just like in the song; big, yellow, crude, empty Tonka toys on the skyline, a line-up in an out-of-town tractor-dealer's lot.

I ask a cowboy called Kenny about them. He is a grizzly, half-garrulous old boy who has a face like a trapper's and stands out by not dancing in a club that prides itself on its dance-preparedness. Kenny is sitting with an even older man, a late septuagenarian sitting sucking hunchedly and toothlessly on bottles of mild. 'A hell-raiser,' says Kenny about the old boy, and the old man guffaws in such a wild and dirty way that it's not clear whether Kenny is talking about his past or his present.

He looks past his sell-by, but who knows? Perhaps he is the Lothario of the beetle-drive circuit.

Kenny tells me about his own past. He was born and bred in Roche, but, unusually for the village, his father didn't work in the china clay pits, as most Roche-ites have over the years, refining the precious clay from the sand and the mica; his father worked in the mines, going off to Africa, from where he returned only once a year. 'Once a year in a good year,' he qualifies gutturally. 'Is there a country called Lagos, over there in Africa?' he asks. For the sake of argument, I nod. 'Well, Lagos – that's where he was.' Kenny's future brought nothing so exotic; he went into the china clay works, and ended up driving those hunks of heavy metal I'd seen for fifteen, twenty years. 'They're fifty-ton trucks,' he mutters, 'a hundred tons loaded.' And everything had gone all right until one day he took a notion that one of them might turn over on him: and that notion struck him while he was driving along the edge of the precipice in the works. He had to stop; to stop on the precipice, and to stop driving altogether. Whatever reaction he sees in my face he doesn't like; he looks at me contemptuously. 'It's known,' he says, 'as a nervous breakdown.'

The extraction company gave him a few months to sort himself out, but when he didn't, or wasn't able to, they paid him off, cheaply and abruptly. And as he lay about the house in a lethargy, his wife decided to up and leave him. The end of the story is brutally short; it happens in just the time it takes Ray Daniels to bridge between 'Tonight the Bottle Let Me Down' and 'Even Whisky (Cannot Ease the Hurt in Me)'. Kenny, silent, sips his third beer – it's 8 p.m. – and will say no more about it. But he will say that he doesn't like sad songs. 'Pah,' he says as he looks grimly into the distance. 'I like Bluegrass. Cajun. Something with a bit of life.'

The next number is 'I Wanna Dance with You', a rare, cheery love-song of John Prine's; something with a bit of life. It has meaning for me, that one, something way back in the past. I smile, but I see that the grimace is still heavy on Kenny's face. Whisky, dancing – none of these things can ease that hurt in him. Maybe love can do it; if it can strike a second time in the life of such a lonesome cowboy as Kenny is; or, for that matter, I am.

'There's a Tear in My Beer'

Left, I don't hit the bottle, as all those cheated on in C&W songs are supposed to do. (There's a whole mule-train of boozing numbers, of course. There's Hank's 'There's a Tear in My Beer', from the lachrymose school of the early days; there are the honky-tonking numbers in which people try to melt their memories, like 'Tonight the Bottle Let Me Down' itself; there are those convenient songs, like 'Swinging Doors', in which men, kicked out of the house, become bar-dwellers, and songs in which, less conveniently, women complain that men are doing so without bothering to wait to be kicked out, like 'I'm Gonna Hire a Wino to Decorate Our Home'; there's 'Two Doors Down' and 'Pass the Paper Bag' and 'The American Honky-Tonk Bar Association'; and, of course, there's the complete *œuvre* of Moe Bandy.)

No – I stay clear of the bar-room, by and large. Stuck in the house, stuck with the children, I try other games, other strategies. Above all, I gather around me every friend I've ever had, and, unshyly and ruthlessly, have them coming over mornings, afternoons and evenings; and when Mohammed can't come, the mountain is only too happy to pack its brood into the camper and descend on Mohammed. But a million Mohammeds can't dissolve a heartache; they can only relieve the symptoms, not attack the disease, which needs a space and a time to cure, and in that sense Mohammeds turn out to be just like booze. Beyond the relief of distraction and the inner assurance of support, they don't really work; and even if you miss out on the morning-after headache, you don't get to sleep so easily when you're left in that raw single solitude that arrives with the night.

Perhaps it's that raw solitude, or the thought of it, that creates the tension between Ruby and me in these early months. It's odd; the day she decides to leave we are amicable, and we spend the afternoon (innocently) in bed, gallows-joking with each other; and the next day I walk her to the station so that she can catch a train to go and tell her parents, encouraging her to be proud of her decision, reassuring her that they will understand it is the right one. We enact various schemes, cooperatively drawn-up; she agrees to keep me and the children going for a while with a generous whack of her salary, and I agree to go out three evenings a week so that she can come in and spend after-work time with the children. But as the weeks pass, and problems begin to appear, the central cruelty of a divorce-with-children becomes obvious. Just when pain should be keeping you apart, business brings you together; just when the exhaustive pre-split analysis has proved your utter incompatibility in any region anywhere near the heart, you are obliged to deal together with issues that relate to your children and therefore sit as close to your heart as it's possible to be.

During this time I go out, on Tuesdays, Thursdays and Saturdays; and I go out with the friends I've ruthlessly arranged to see. And I sit through the early part of the evening telling them my woes, and they listen and support and do all the things that good friends do. And by the time I return at 9.30 or 10 p.m. (I have to get back by then or Ruby will turn me into a pumpkin) I've had a couple of drinks, and am feeling not only talkative, but pretty bloody justified, too. A few times, especially if there's football on the telly, I do manage just to say goodnight, and off she goes into the night. But more often than not, by the time I'm home, I'm raring to go; maybe something about the way she's dealing with the kids has annoyed me, and it starts from that; but what I really want to do is prove to her that since I'm right (I was left, I did nothing wrong, I'm picking up the pieces children-wise) and she's wrong (she fucked off, she wouldn't go to counselling, they crawl into *my* bed at night) I have an inalienable moral right to say how things should be done from now on.

How can I convey the feeling of endlessness and futility that you have when you start going down that path? Tregeagle had it easy, that's all I'll say, for Dozmare was a paddling-pool compared to the depth of resentment that the wish to take control of your own life seems to engender. The arguments bang back and forth, with voices raised and then softened, arguments accepted and then rejected. It extends beyond the evening itself into the next day; you live life discovering rapier replies which prove to be blunt when your opponent is thickly armoured by the process of having left you; you don't work the next day, or the next, because you're sitting at the desk writing letters and memos and faxes that burn their way down your fingertips and on to the screen. And in the end, after months of it, you find you're no further forward; the things we're arguing for are going to be held fast to, for she needs to build walls around her new life and I need to shore up the ones that sit around the remains of my old one.

I realize this some months into the process, and, one revolutionary night, I ask her for ten minutes and set out a theory: that, since we are never going to agree on even the most minor point of fact in respect of the demise of our relationship and what happened to it, we should at least agree to respect that the other person's point of view is never going to change; that we should acknowledge that we occupy parallel universes which do not impinge on one another; that what we must do is accept this, and then, with those parallel concrete blocks deep-set in our brains, working like coastal defences to repel the daily D-Days of resentment, we will be able to move forward, in a superior way, on the important issues: the children, the house, the money.

But whether she just can't see it, or whether she's involved in a moral argument of her own, with much higher stakes, or whether it's just that, by the time I get there, she's so resentful at being held back night after night, I don't know. At any rate the arguments continue. In the end, I take unilateral action; I buy a big poster of Buddha and hang it on the staircase, looking at it every morning, ready and willing to endure any indignity and to respond to it with calm indifference. *In every day, in every way*, is my mantra. *No matter what* . . . And from this point – it's about three or four months into the separation – I resolve to keep my nose clean, to ensure that, should we ever come to court, I will not be accusable in terms of having made things excessively difficult for her. At this point I make it easier for her to take the children away, I stop slagging off the Greek, I go to bed when I come in at night. In fact, I feel that from this point, however much things hurt me, I do little wrong, though I suspect that Ruby occupies a parallel universe on that one.

Round here, son, they call me wee Pete wi' the big guitar . . .

It's deep into Texas Express's third set at the Texas Star, or perhaps deep into Texas Star's third set at the Texas Express: I'm catching a fast black home later, so I've had a couple, and, just as the girls get prettier around closing time, so do the names get harder to distinguish. Vic, holder of the Bret Maverick trophy, gets up and makes an announcement in best MC pastiche – *Lay-deez and gennulmen! Tonight's charity singer* . . . *All the way from Nashville, Tennessee (via the Gorbals)* . . . *A big hand, please, for GRAND-PA PER-KINS!* – and a man appears on stage in a one-piece piece of hillbilly underwear, that droopy long-john sort with the saggy bum-flap and the long buttoned fly.

After he's finished singing, Veronica takes me into the side room that serves as backstage, and we have our photos taken – Vic, Veronica, Grandpa Perkins and me. Grandpa Perkins's fly-buttons keep coming undone, and Vic poses for the camera aiming his six-gun at Grandpa Perkins's groin. Grandpa Perkins, showman, loves every minute of it; he cracks jokes about how the prints will need the curly bits cut off. Later, back in the hall, he appears in mufti, a red polo shirt and a Nashville baseball cap. He's a short, solid man, about forty-five or fifty, I'd say, with a pint in his hand: 'Veronica says you're writing a book? I could write your book for ye . . .' It seems like a good offer, so I arrange to go round to his place the next day. Grandpa Perkins, aka Muskrat, aka Pete, lives in Hamilton, and I find his place all right, even though all I can remember of the directions that bleary, headachy morning is that I have to turn right by a gasometer.

A mansion on the hill it isn't. Pete lives at the top of a three-storey block of flats, not lovely by any means, though not as grimy as some; we're in one of those Lanarkshire towns – like Airdrie, like Motherwell – that was put into a long shadow when the Ravenscraig Steelworks closed. Like many Scottish flat-dwellers, Pete retains the old tenement habit of hanging out the window, keeping an eye on things – 'Where's your car?' he asks, going to the balcony. 'Oh, aye, the VW.' He's wearing the same gear as last night – the polo-shirt and his jeans – though he's got slippers on. He seems more nervous now, and I realize that his performance adrenalin has faded; he's back to being ordinary in the dull light of the morning.

He takes me through to his bedroom. Lying around are a load of mementoes and programmes, as well as accessories – stetsons, bandannas, T-shirts. He pulls out a guitar-case and opens it for me to have a look and, when I look avaricious, a feel. The guitar, a whacking great Jumbo, is stunningly beautiful: 'A Gibson J200 Flat Top,' says Pete, 'the King of the Flat Tops.' He gives me a potted history, both of the instrument (first made 1938, used on film by Elvis in *Loving You*) and of his instrument (ordered specially from McCormick's in the mid-1960s, now worth about £3,000). It's a distinctive machine that marks him out from the other performers around. 'Round here, son,' he says, 'they call me wee Pete wi' the big guitar . . .'

We wander back into the lounge, but the phone rings and he has to go out the room to answer it. While he's away, I wander over to his hi-fi stand, which has a row of records about three feet wide. I've got two feet along by the time he comes back, but I haven't come across a single record not by George Jones. 'Seventy-eight albums,' he says, and he begins to pull them out one by one for me to examine. I watch George's haircut sprout from fifties crewcut into seventies bouffant; watch his sideburns recede from sixties extravagance into eighties sobriety. And after a few minutes it's clear: Pete wants to talk about George Jones, while I want to talk about Pete. So in the end we reach a compromise. He digs out a videobiography – of George, of course, not of himself – and we begin chawing as Celtic and Aberdeen, replaying from the night before on Sky, give way to pictures of George's toothless Texan rural relatives and a Nashville narrator with an orchestrated, slickly metropolitan delivery: 'The strain of the Great Depression,' the rich voice oozes, 'with its attendant poverty, lay heavily on the rural settle- ments. Only family, children, and, of course, music seemed to have the power to sweep away the dark clouds . . .'

Pete had had his share of dark clouds when he heard George first in 1955, when he was fifteen. He had already left school, was already in the shipyards, was already apprenticed as a welder when 'Why Baby Why?' knocked him off his feet. But if his childhood ended abruptly, it's still remembered fondly as a time filled with music. 'My ma and da were country fans. I used to go to bed to the sound of Jimmie Rodgers; my father would play Jimmie Rodgers all the time. Jimmie Rodgers, "the Singing Brakeman". And he would take me to the Empire; I saw Big Bill Campbell there. He had a singer called Peggy and a yodeller called Norman, and he'd come on and sit on a wee totty barrel and he'd go' – Pete mimics an an extravagant drawl – ' "miiii-ghty fine . . ." The first words he would say: "This is the Big Bill Campbell Show – Miiii-ghty Fiii-ne." '

In the background, on the TV, we're back in Saratoga, Texas, back in the Great Depression with the dust blowing across the plains. George's grandmaw is on, teaching him to play chords. (Needless to say, honky-tonking was not in her mind; she wanted him to play devotional music.) We flash forward to the mid-fifties, and George, first crewcutted, then complete with spiky flat-top, has found another direction; like Conway, who came back to C&W, and like Elvis, who didn't, George is flirting with rock 'n' roll. A suitably ridiculous clip of him gyrating appears, and the voice schmaltzes on: 'For a moment there, George lost touch with the music that had filled his life . . . but it wasn't long before country called again. And when country calls, even George Jones has to listen . . .'

'There's George. Look!' says Pete, pointing at the screen recognizingly, as if George's countryless period was a time in disguise. We watch on, and he chats. 'Yeah,' says Pete. 'I bought a guitar at nineteen. I was mucking about in the house with my pals; this was '58, '59, and skiffle was all the rage. I learned to play C, F and G, which was all you needed; I would sit there every night till my fingers bled. I would get a wee bottle of methylated spirits and stick my fingers in to harden the skin up. So when I was a young journeyman, in the shipyards, about twenty, I used to bring my guitar in and play. I would go into the pubs and play. Or I would take my guitar up to the back seat of the tram-cars and play. There were a lot of people interested; the sixties and seventies were great times for country in Glasgow. People could relate to what we were singing about. They'll never come back, they days. There's George. Look!'

There's George, indeed; rock 'n' roll has come and gone, he's put gospel on the back-burner, and now he's beginning to take his heartbreak numbers into the Texas roadhouses and honky-tonks. He begins to get a name and is contracted to do doubleheaders with Buck Owens, King of the Bakersfield Sound. The tape tells a nice story: George is always on second, and Buck is getting 'mighty pissed' at the order of service. George says, 'Buck, if you want me to go out first I'll go out first, but let me tell you that when I come off you won't even want to go out there.' Buck insists George go on first. George does – and plays Buck's set, word for word, riff for riff, in its entirety; he goes on stage, in other words, and does Buck's show. And he comes off stage and he looks over to Buck and he says, 'Your turn . . .' And even if Buck is still more 'pissed', well, he forgives him, and soon, as the sixties begin to swing, George is on stage at the Grand Ole Opry, the Music City Mecca.

Pete spent the sixties in a band called the Longhorns. 'We played all over Glasgow. Everywhere and anywhere.' He gets out his photo album. There's a list of musicians at the front, people who've come and gone from his bands; sundry Jimmys and Dougies and Georges and Gerrys and the odd Ann-Marie. In the shots, the Jimmys and the Dougies and the rest are wearing outfits that wouldn't pass muster amongst modern-day westerners; the hats are shallow, the shirts collarless, the trousers corduroy. 'Look at the tooled boots,' says Pete. 'They were rare in they days.' I ask him if they were imported; this was before stacked heels were a fashion item, before Nike Air made manly footwear. 'The hats came from Dunn's in Glasgow,' says Pete. 'I don't know about the boots, but they were dear. Tooled boots were dear.'

He runs through the photographs, pointing out the backgrounds, mentioning various spots where he had gigs; while George was playing Vegas or Charleston or Memphis or Louisville, Pete was in pub back rooms in Glasgow. 'That one's the Duck Bay Marina. A wee lounge in Blantyre.' Another page is turned. 'That's Jimmy Johnstone's pub. You know him? The winger. Played with Celtic. He's lost all his money now.' Another page. 'That's a house in Barrhead, I canny mind the name of it now.' Another page. 'That's the Bowler's. The famous pub for country was always the Bowler's. They had a big mural there, with Johnny Cash and Hank Williams on it.'

Some of the pictures have signatures on them; on one there's Jim Reeves, on another Hank Snow. For a moment I think he is going to say that Jim or Hank had come down to the Bowler's, but no; one of the Gerrys, the bassist, had waited in line outside the stage-door of the Apollo or the Empire or the Playhouse. Isabel, Pete's wife, begins to appear in the snaps, first singing ('She's a great singer, though very shy'), then eight months pregnant with their son. Did Pete sense he was never going to *be* George when he called his son Paul George Jones Perkins? Who knows? The Longhorns kept going, though. 'We were well known in Glasgow. A household name, in fact . . .'

As Isabel delivers Paul George Jones Perkins, George is marrying Tammy Wynette, then descending into a pool of drink and drugs; we're in the seventies and eighties now, and the flares are out in force, ballooning their way across the bottom of the screen. George gets unreliable, once disappearing for three weeks at a time off a tour with law-suits from promoters and organizers flying as wildly as the bottoms of a pair of hipsters; as Paul George Jones Perkins is christened, George rechristens himself – in song – No-Show Jones. The narrator schmaltzes up George's ten-year bender with a convenient bit of honky-tonk mythology based on the fact that George would sometimes, having missed a big concert-hall gig, turn up and play in a small beer-joint somewhere in rural Texas. 'George was on the run from the star-system, and was heading back to play for the people who mattered to him most . . .'

Pete, on the run from the star-system himself, is moved by the sight of George in his cups: 'Just look at him – is that no' sad?' Up on screen comes George, playing 'He Stopped Loving Her Today' in a state of befuddlement that makes those shots of the drug-crazed Elvis look like the Presley body is a temple as stimulant-free as that of an oompah-man in a Sally Army band. 'Look at the state of him there,' says Pete, with sympathy.

On TV, George gets the 1981 Male Vocalist of the Year at some event in Nashville. 'He's away wi' the birds here,' says Pete, as George staggers on to the stage, speaks incomprehensibly and staggers off in the wrong direction. 'He talks a load of rubbish in this,' says Pete. 'Just wait till you hear him talking . . .' A pause, as we watch. 'Look at him here! Down to 105 pounds. Look at him . . . he looks like one of these guys that's just been released from prison, or from a work-camp by the Japs. Look at him! A wee totty body and a big heid . . .'

Pete was not staying still either. 'In 1983 I went to Australia,' he says. 'Emigrated. Following my trade; I was offered a job in an Australian shipyard working on submarines. I was still singing, and I wrote a lot of songs there, when I was working in the yards; I used to write about these submarines we were sending to sea. We built a ship called the *Successful*, and to celebrate I wrote a song called "The Ballad of the Unsuccessful", as well as some others. I never use them now. I never sing them now; they're no use. But I did play a lot over there; and I toured. In fact, I was known as the Australian George Jones. I was doing well. But in the end I had to come back – the heat was driving me demented . . .'

The tape is moving into tribute mode; we've had the happy ending (George's car-plate, NO-SHOW JONES, has been swapped for one saying I DO SHOW) and we see him playing a concert at the Knoxville Coliseum. It's recent, from about '93, and it's the audience that is going demented. 'That's just brilliant,' says Pete. 'After what George has been through – three times in the hospital, an alcoholic, so many marriages, all the rest of it . . . you'd think he wouldn't be able to sing – you'd think he'd be deid by now . . .' As 'Bartender's Blues' plays, talking heads roll up to sing George's praises. Johnny Cash's answer to who's the greatest country singer is, apparently, 'What, besides George Jones?' A hundred other Nashville faces say the same thing in different words. And Cash returns to tell of Elvis Costello, apparently smashed out of his head after he'd been in Nashville to record *Almost Blue*, standing on a table loudly describing Jones as 'THE GREATESHT COUNTRY SHINGER IN THE HISHTRY OF THE WORLD . . .'

Pete has not worked since he came home. He has begun to play again around Glasgow; trying to kick himself into life, but it's hard to get bookings; he passes me his card, on which he's called Muskrat and on which he offers to play old or new country for any occasion. Isabel comes in and they sing to me in the front room; it's a duet, a George Jones–Melba Montgomery thing called 'We Must Have Been Out of Our Minds'. It is genuinely stunning; an achingly beautiful performance, in spite of the sixties flat front room, in spite of long dark-haired Isabel's crippling shyness that makes her look at, and practically chew, the carpet. Pete's voice is George's voice to perfection, is indistinguishable from what's been on the tape, with its small falsetto catch in the throat. I ask Pete if he's made any recordings, if he's a tape I can have. 'No. I never made records. You see, I can't stand the sound of my own voice. I don't think I'm good enough.'

We sit quietly for a while; I can't really find the words to tell them how good they are, and how unjust it is that two lives 5,000 miles apart can dovetail so exactly; exactly, that is, up to the point that George goes on to make seventy-eight albums and live in a mansion on the hill, while Pete lives in a first-right-by-the-gasometer place in Hamilton. And I have to scroll through in my mind what has been said, genuinely unaware of what is reality and what is fantasy, unclear about how one story has rubbed off on the other. I know that Pete has not made all this up. But all that's missing from Pete's life is the Tammy years, the demented part of life when George's brain was wasted by booze and pills and ended up talking in a quacking voice, like Donald Duck's.

I get ready to go. We're standing by the door, and I'm thinking about his complete lack of bitterness that George and he, practically indistinguishable, have had destinies so different. I ask him a question I'd been asking everybody in Glasgow that week; why do country people, who seem so hugely content, favour lyrics with such a high misery quotient? How did they come by their assured happiness, and how does the music fit? The response is a torrent; it's the story of his first marriage, which fills in the missing pieces and provides the final link between big George and wee Pete. For Pete had married at nineteen, the first time round; and he'd had three kids by the time his wife left him, taking them with her. Up to then Pete had been a sportsman, the son of a Powderhall professional sprinter; Pete himself was a footballer, in training, fit. But he stopped training and started drinking when he stopped seeing his kids; and before very long, he was hitting Skid Row, the bottle letting him down plenty of times, the bartender frequently the recipient of his blues.

'You see, I know about heartbreak,' he says, 'and two things saved me. She' – he points at Isabel – 'was one of them. And the other was country music. I took up playing country then, and it was through playing that I pulled myself up, got myself back on the tracks. And, son, that's why George – and Hank for that matter – are good, are worth listening to. If you listen to their voices you can hear it, can't you? Those guys have been there. They know what it's all about. They know what a heartbreak is. And it's the same with me . . .' And I realize, humbly, that it is the same with him; that the assuredness comes from having climbed back up the mountain; from knowing what's at the bottom and how it's different from what's half-way up.

He's off the booze now, is Pete, 'back to normal', as he says; one day at a time. The music is no less valuable, though; the knowledge of pain affirms the happiness of the present. He'd like help, though; he's been trying to write a novel ('I've got pages and pages scribbled in there, you should see it') and he doesn't know quite what to do with it. I say various sensible things and ask him what it's all about. 'Basically it's about a Scottish country singer – me, if you like – who turns up in

Nashville in the fifties. And Buck Owens is there, and Hank Snow is there, and George Jones is there – and soon these guys are looking over their shoulders because they know somebody good is coming right up behind them.' Various adventures follow; they feature mansions, Cadillacs and a flat-top Jumbo guitar. 'I don't know if anything'll come of it,' Pete says, and he adds, self-deprecatingly: 'A fantasy, you'd call it.'

A broken lady, waiting to be mended . . .

'You just wait till Saturday. Saturday's the big one,' says Siringo, a gunfighter down from Dunfermline for the week. He should know; he's been coming to Witton Castle, to the Great Northern Festival, for years. It's Thursday tonight; the festival goes on until Sunday. And maybe those present are drinking to escape; it's not clear. But it is clear that in a 250-foot tent full of a hundred longways tables that look like they've been transplanted direct from the country clubs of Ashington and Hartlepool and Whitley Bay, three-quarters of those present are out of their heads. It's only half-past nine, but already the tables are swaying, as Colt 45, Geordie lads themselves, are giving it that bar-room shoutalong standard which north-easternizes as 'Where Am I Going to Live When I Get Whoam?'

Other bands are in tune with the spirit of the evening too. Custer's Last Band, over from Northern Ireland, have chipped in a boozer or two, and so have Jolene and Barry, down from Falkirk, and now a Manchester duo called Grace and Nash are playing the 'Swinging Doors' routine for all it's worth. 'Anyone here from Seaton?' Grace or Nash shouts. 'YEAH!' 'Peterlee?' 'YEAH!' 'North Shields?' 'YEAH!' 'Then let's have a party!' They sing a song called 'Corn Whisky', and about what a state it left them in; everyone claps along to the bluegrassy solo. 'This is for the real men and the alcoholics,' calls Nash or Grace as he introduces a dance-number; and after the dance is over, when it's finished, Grace or Nash laughs: 'I didn't see many real men.' 'AWWWWWWWW.' 'I saw plenty of alcoholics, though!' 'YEAH!'

I know that on another night, at another time, I would laugh at all this, down a pint or three, get cordial, do a bit of table-swaying myself, see what happens. But tonight it's not so easy, because early on the morning of the Monday before, a woman I know came over to the house to tell me that her husband had passed the hours of the night just gone by beating her all around the house; and that he had done this after returning from an all-day festival just such as the Great Northern one is; and watching Seaton and Peterlee and South Shields in action, I can't get away from the idea that at ten the night before he was downing a pint or three and getting cordial and doing a bit of swaying, but that when it came to seeing what happened – well, that did.

So I watch the dressed-up good-timing with a slightly jaundiced eye. I watch a man from Morecambe, in black frock-coat, play the Drunken Undertaker, measuring up a cowboy for a coffin with a piece of string; the cowboy has a gun in the holster on one side of his belt and a mobile phone on the other. I feel bad on my own account – a small, self-pitying bit of me remembers that my friend had come over three days before the wedding, not much more than a year before, and asked me whether I thought she should marry him; and, as you do, I bolstered and blustered and said that it was just nerves and that she should go ahead. But I also feel the horror of what actually happens to people, what occurs when you get beyond myths and jokes, what it's like for Patsy when Charlie beats her. My friend's morning-after face, shocked and pale and silent, is stuck in my head and talks eloquently of what it's like when drink turns home into hell, when you suffer pain no country song can do justice to.

Curiously enough, when Ruby left me, my friend and her husband were a couple I looked at with envy: lively, active, sorted. But when we talk on the Monday, the story is different;

it spills out over a long and searing time. Things had been okay, just as presented, when they first moved in together. He had encouraged her decision to set up her own business from home; he had offered to support her while she got things going. But quickly he had begun to resent the financial inequity, and he habitually left her without money for the day, and sometimes – if he was going away – for the week. He was uncommunicative sexually; he was capable of lust and its fulfilment, but he wouldn't hold her at any other time, and he fantasized relentlessly about friends and dreamed of an open arrangement. He became unable to pass an evening without spliffing up – not socially, not for a specific buzz, but relentlessly in that way that makes people's brains into cabbage, whatever they may think; and, of course, he had begun to drink himself into slurry of an evening, almost every evening.

She, meanwhile, had got into that abused state where you present the world outside with an image of super-normality; I'd seen it myself, before, in the impeccably tidy house a colleague's battered wife kept when I was a teacher; but never saw it there, in her; never saw how she refused to say what things were wrong, for fear that I, or others, would ask why she was still there when the hardest thing, as Ruby knows, is to face what you feel and act to change. But unlike Ruby, she had to face a rough-and-ready reckoning. He went festivalling to celebrate a new job, or something, and presumably did so with all the adjusted geniality he displayed to the outside world; and then he came home from the festival smashed out of his mind, found her sullen and beat the shit out of her.

When she arrives that morning she is reluctant to talk; she knows there was an argument when he first arrived home, and that she can be sassy in the extreme, so maybe she should blame herself. I do my best, and keep insisting she resist victimhood, and once the whole story is told, there is no possibility of what happened being anything but a gross act of abuse. When the argument heated up – when push turned to shove – he began to shove, and punch, and kick. She refused to lie down in front of it, so he kept going. He aimed his punches for a place that he knew, given her medical history, was a dangerous place for her. He dragged her upstairs to the bathroom and, having pissed his bladderful into the pan, thrust her head down it; and then fell, unconscious, into a deep sleep.

And yet the image that lived with her was not necessarily of what happened in the night; in all sorts of ways she could find an explanation for those things that would have allowed them to stay together, at least until things were sorted out. But when he woke, and she asked him to take the day off work and talk about what happened, he refused, and put his genial, outside-world face back on and went out to work as normal; and when she pleaded for money so that she could go and find someone to talk to – a real friend, not just me who knew her and happened to live in the same town, but a real friend who went back further – he chucked her, in small change, the grand sum of £1.37 – enough for ten fags without matches which, he suggested, was all the support she needed. And those images in the end became the unforgivable ones when she decided, some weeks later, that the marriage was over.

Grace and Nash have a conflab. 'Any trashy women here tonight?' 'YEAH!' Whichever one it is that sings sings a Gatlin Brothers number about a broken lady waiting to be mended, and never has this C&W medium seemed so inadequate for the ghastliness of things. The Nanci Griffith number they strum up next, with the line about John Wayne on the *Late Late Show* saving the girl and riding away, just makes me feel how inadequate a Mohammed I am. I resolve to do better when I get whoam, and feel a wash of tenderness. Then, foolishly, I sit outside the marquee for a bit and watch the families frolic. Innocent enough, there's a boy in a Newcastle strip kicking a football on to the roof, and a girl in a bridesmaid's dress systematically shooting all her friends with a pop-gun. But there's also boys of ten and eleven being fed Newcastle Brown by their fathers or grandfathers, and it's hard to see what kind of husbands they'll turn out to be, when a morning-suited bridegroom could appear so much one thing outside another sort of tent and, bottled, descend into barbarity in, as they say, the comfort of the home.

We don't have the picture on the box. All we've got are the little pieces . . .

Ernie is not a drinker, that's plain to see; and though he does break off from the Portsmouth dance-floor to pop a pill or two, the pills are for his angina, not his psyche. If he has an escapist addiction, it's to C&W dancing, to old-style free-style dancing in couples. But he has another opiate too; for Ernie the free-style dancer by night is Ernie the freelance spiritual healer by day.

Sitting at a table with his friends – one of them is a dead-ringer for George Jones, bizarrely enough – we talk about music and dancing for a bit. Like many of his age, he found country while serving in the RAF on US air bases in Italy; there he heard Jimmie 'Singing Brakeman' Rodgers and the rest, and a lifetime obsession began. He's scornful of the line-dancers who, he thinks, are taking over too many country clubs. (Many clubs have had to develop etiquettes – line-dancers in this part of the floor, western dancers in another – to ease tension but, even so, Ernie has, on one occasion, had his twinkly features threatened with rearrangement by a powerfully built female liner.)

I ask him what he thinks of the latest pro-line theory, that the dancers originated amongst cowboys jigging partnerlessly while out on the drive. 'I've been a western film fanatic sixty-odd years,' he says, 'from Gene Autry on. And the idea of tough, hairy, range-hardened cowboys prancing around in lines, circles, squares, linking arms . . .' He doesn't need to finish the sentence to express his contempt; and watching him twinkle round the floor with his Hampshire lady-friend (he has another, of a more serious sort, down in Somerset) and seeing the line-dancers doing their stuff in another corner of the room – well, it's clear that couple-dancing is the more human form, that line-dancing, with all its moves and routines and fancy stepping, is a technical, not a romantic, art.

Ernie tells me of his working life. He used to promote country bands – he sold British acts with American names (the Midnite Ramblers, the Rangemen) to Hampshire naval bases; and between promotions turned his hand to a load of things to keep the wolf from the door: painting and decorating, insurance agency, civil servitude, repping for a brewery – 'Lovely job,' he says – shop management, car-selling, carpet warehousing. He's been a hard-working man in his time, it's clear; and woven through this life of toil is a thread of emotional toil; as a boy, in 1935, he cradled a young sister dying of rheumatic bruising; as a man, in 1947, he cradled his young wife, Nellie, who was dying of tuberculosis.

Enough heartache for one life, one would have thought, but there's no experiential furrow on his brow as he resumes his dance, his small frame moving easily and flashily. Such help as he needed came not from the bottle but from the paranormal; not from spirits but from the spiritual. While laid up in hospital with a fractured skull after a cycling accident – and he does have the grace to wonder out loud whether what follows originated in that bump on his head – he began to read of UFOs and little green men and alien abductions. Up and about again – out and about again – he began to have experiences.

As the band takes five he talks me through the stages of his visions. First, a 'glowing cigar' appearing in the air above Portsdown Hill, hanging in the air until a pair of RAF meteor jets appeared, then – 'like someone switching off a light-bulb' – disappearing. Then, a series of big, triangular apparitions above his garden – close enough and real enough for him to see the rivets, witnessed by his new wife and by four music-fiend friends driving to a gig along the M27. 'Watching,' he says, 'I had a strange vision of all the stars and planets stretching out; and seeing a light at the end of the chain. And that vision changed my life in seconds. I changed from one day to the next. I understood nature, flowers, birds. The earth was full of life under my feet, even the stones. I found something in a book that describes it: *Thou canst not pick a flower without thou disturbest a stone.* And that was just how I felt.

'In 1979,' he continues – and his eye is glittering now, not twinkling, an Ancient Mariner of the C&W dance-scene – 'a friend of mine got cancer of the stomach. I looked after him for a while – washed him and fed him. And after a bit he said he wanted to go to a healer, and I ended up going with him.' Once there, Ernie was persuaded to join in the process, and, when various paranormal bizarrities manifested themselves in the room (a crucifix passed through a box, and the friend's dead father spoke familiarly to them) he was persuaded to join in the process long-term. Cures followed; and as his second wife, jealous of his other world, left him, his first returned: 'I fell asleep under a tree in the garden, and dreamed of a lovely, lovely light doing intimate things to my body. And when I woke, there was a tanned woman sitting in front of me saying, "All these years you've been asleep – and now you're awake." Well, I knew it was my Nellie. And since then I've stopped seeing UFOs; since my cosmic experience, I've looked inside; that's where my universe is.'

I'm – well, I'm just as you would be when such stories spout out; but Ernie holds me as he tells me how he once brought his powers to the C&W dance-floor. 'It was 1988, Christmas week. I was on my own, divorced, at that stage; and I decided to go down to a club I used to go to in Portsmouth, where I hadn't been for ten years. I got talking to a man and wife at my table, and after a while I asked the woman, "Would you like to have a little dance, m'dear?" And she said, "Sorry, but I've got five discs gone in my back; I've been this way thirty years. I can't dance; I only came up here because I like this band." So I said to her, "Come with me for a little dance," and I took her on to the dance-floor. They were playing a song called "On the Other Hand", I remember, and as we danced around I was moving my hand up and down her back and I was laughing because I knew I had to concentrate on the healing, but I also had to make sure my feet were going the right way.

'We walked off the floor and I said, "How do you feel?" And she said, "Not bad." And I tell you, within ten minutes she was back on the floor with me, then with her husband; we even did some rock 'n' rolling, and I made sure I twisted her round. I said to her as we came off, "I don't normally say this, but I'm sure – this will last the rest of your life." And about three months later, at Easter, I met her at the club, and when she appeared she flung her arms around me, and she said, "You really have changed my life." And I really had, because a few months later I heard that she'd left her husband and run off with a bloke twenty years her junior! So obviously' – he gives a salacious look – 'her back must have been better . . .'

The band is back on stage, Ernie's lady-friend is waiting expectantly, and his addiction can't wait; he disappears on to the dance-floor. I get a beer from the bar and stand watching him, and he's a real charmer; attentive to his partner yet, like a child on a carousel, flashing me a smile every time the waltz brings him round to my side of the room. He has to break for a second to get himself another angina pill, and that gives him a moment to sign off: 'If you think about all that stuff – now, who put the pieces of all that together? Here was this woman with a bad back who came all the way from Sussex because her favourite band was playing at my club; and I hadn't been to the club for ten years, but I turn up that night and sit at her table. She gets cured. Who put all that together? It's a vast jigsaw, you know. Like I said to her, "We don't have the picture on the box. All we've got are all the little pieces."' And he moves off again; the drugs course his veins but it's the dance that takes his sorrow away.

Yorkshire had the cowboys, America had only the
Indians . . .

White-line fever, Merle Haggard calls it, an addiction to the
road. But when Haggard sings it, that sickness right down deep
within his soul gets somewhere near being a positive; there's a
romance of a sort if you have reasons of your own for not letting
your hat rest on the same peg too long, when the open road,
gypsy-like, holds more romance than lying on the sofa and
having some pretty lady rub your back. But when that idea
seems hopeless, an impossible fantasy . . .

Tonight, winding across the blasted moors of North Yorkshire,
the addiction has gone cold turkey on me. I'm sick of this life of
petrol pumps and crawler lanes and tanker washes, sick of the
lost highway. I wish there was someone I'd just left, someone
I'd be going back to tonight, but there's just the van and the
night and the music. RAW – 1 MILE, says the sign by the
road; it feels like a lot closer than that. And if the beauties of
the northern moors have no consolation, what chance the urban
sprawl of Middlesbrough? At Billingham the windscreen is full
of pylons pointing to where the fat ICI coolers and their tall
chemical chimneys chuck a darkness at the big sky. It would be
a *White Heat* landscape, but it's just too dirty; nothing but miles
and miles of gushing pipes and girders; the only light is from
the Southern Cross, and that's a pub.

I sit outside the Malleable Club in Stockton-on-Tees, not
knowing whether I can face it. Malleable; what you have to be
to be here? Or to live here? The name sticks out from the other
local ones with its suggestion of persistence; it's not the Broken
Horseshoe up the road nor the Broken G at Guisborough. Or
maybe it's just the sort of materials men round here work on;
after all, this is the place where the football team is called
Synthonia, a word so apparently full of harmony that even
'United' can't compete, until you find out that the key product in

these parts, and the basis of ICI's work, is Synthetic Ammonia.

Finally I go in and I find sympathy at the first port of call. 'I've been a travelling man,' says Tommy. 'I know what it's like.' Tommy is a small man in jeans, a black hat and a waistcoat, practically the only cowboy in a room full of quiet, appreciative but characterless C&W listeners. He's seventy and has just this week cut off a long, white hillbilly beard. Stubbled only, his face looks like Spike Milligan's. He has spent his life as a joiner, following the money all round the south of England; he did the wood in a Catholic church in Guildford I've seen, and it's beautiful. He remembers being on sites, living in a caravan for winters on end, a routine of heavy dumpers and brew-ups, of JCBs and pots of tea. They sound like happy years, now, though the tedium and shiftlessness pop into his voice from time to time. Whatever – his medium now is the travelling song: Haggard's 'Fugitive' numbers; Willie Nelson's train-song 'The City of New Orleans'; anything by Boxcar Willie; he hums a line from my old favourite about being next of kin to the wayward wind, and he makes it sound nice again. He tells me why his travelling came to an end; how his mother started to die, so he had to come home and face down what had driven him away. 'She held the purse-strings, you see . . .'

The purse-strings were worth the loosening, as it turned out, for this cowboy came from a family of successful butchers. His grandfather had set them up all over the place – in York, in Thirsk, in Hutton Rudby, in several other county locations – and his father had taken them over. His older brothers had taken up the business – 'slaughtering', as Tommy calls it – but he didn't take to it, and he remembers the abattoir with a grimace even now, fifty-five years later; the slitting of the animal, the drenching blood, the boiling water poured into the gaping wound. One day his father called him to bring the boiling water, but no boiling water, and no Tommy, appeared; he was off, out of his familial destiny, away from the stench of death. He opted for woodworking, and his bench-joinery apprenticeship was at an undertaker's. 'It's a good training. If someone dies and you're on your own, well – you just have to get on with it. Seven hours' work, maybe, on your own. It's no use saying to them as wants to buy a burial-box, you'll have to wait until the boss gets back . . .'

So he made 'ten million coffins' before he hit the road; but he made two bad marriages, too. 'You see, it wasn't the slaughtering that drove me away. It was my first two wives. I was glad to be gone.' Asked, he conspicuously fails to deliver the details of that life back then; there's just a sigh, a platitude or two about being young, about not being suited, about finding out too late. But when the long and winding road of the world brought him back home to Yorkshire – 'Did you know that Yorkshire was where the cowboys originated? I read that in a book. Yorkshire had the cowboys, America had only the Indians' – he ran into Margaret, and she's been with him now long enough for children and a grandchild. His pretty, slim daughter – achingly pretty, achingly slim on a night like tonight – plays championship bowls as well as championship line-dancing; and Tommy sits flanked by the two of them, grinning at the way the road, at the end of his journey, has brought him all he could ever have asked for. 'Family, happiness, country music,' he says. 'What could be better? Sitting here, watching the world go by, having a few drinks. And I'll tell you what – I have a private taxi, comes and picks me up, every night. Go anywhere for me, he will. 'Cos I've got some money, you see . . .'

Cynical, I look hard at him. Is there something – not anything admitted, perhaps not even anything real – lurking behind that exterior? The past seems shut out, repressed; the present too pat, too happy. 'It doesn't cost much to be nice,' he insists, eyeing me, 'but it can cost you a lot to be nasty.' Still I search: is there something manic about the way he asks me if I can account for the way that Waylon Jennings and Willie Nelson and George Jones and Hank Williams all took to the drink? He claims never to have hit the bottle: 'A few beers with the boys, of course.

But nothing serious. You see, drinking never made a man. Self-confidence is what makes a man. To me, the important thing is to be a self-made man. A self-made man doesn't need anything to help him up – that's false confidence. And you can't be a self-made man if the drink is what makes you.'

He sounds like a man who knows, and he grins at me as if he hopes that I'll know he knows. As I drive home to an empty bed, I can only hope for the same confidence, for the same self-madeness; in these times of desolation they seem far away, those ideas, as you lurch between one idea and another of what you are, one uncertainty to another about what you should do to meet more people, to find love, to work out a way of things being worthwhile. 'Pass the Paper Bag That Holds the Bottle' is Deliverance's last number, or the last I hear, and by chance in the car I pick up a local station's country hour, and they're having a booze theme, what with 'Friends in Low Places' and 'Drinkin' and Drivin' (That Woman Right Off Of My Mind)'.

Somewhere in Tommy's tale there's a principle of conduct, if only I can find it. I hear him again and again as I cross the moors on the return journey; not the stuff about how he sang on stage with Slim Whitman once, nor the nose-tapping stuff about Willie Nelson's hair not being his own. No; it was his envoi: 'The two greatest things in life,' he says – slurs? – 'are to be able to say no and to have patience.' I whack a tape in, listen to Ernest Tubb for a while. Normally sincere, Ernest's being foxy, something about Daddy scolding him for having too many women for a boy just his size. It's not quite right. For me, it's 'Drinkin' and Drivin' back across the lonely moors; only the likes of Tommy have the comfort of a private taxi waiting at the door.

CHAPTER THREE

Sometimes It's Hard to be a Woman

4,000 silver dollars embedded in the dashboard . . .

If George Jones is my country hero – THE GREATESHT COUNTRY SHINGER IN THE HISHTRY OF THE WORLD, remember – then, in an altogether funnier sort of way, Tammy Wynette is my country heroine. Tammy is not the singer George is but, like George's, Tammy's life is the stuff that all country clichés are built on, in the way that western clichés are (coach-built) on *Stagecoach*.

There are two great statistics in Tammy's life. One concerns the perilously stitched-together nature of her insides; she has had some twenty operations in her fifty-odd years, some of them involving tampering with organs that are deeply vital; yet she goes on playing and playing date after date, year after 200-appearance year, never resting, never assuming she has enough to retire on. (According to myth, she renews her state licence to practise manicure each year, just in case, after decades of stardom and fan-worship, the world goes cold on her.) The other statistic refers, of course, to the number of husbands she has worked her way through. She's always been more partial to 'D-I-V-O-R-C-E' than to standing by her man; and if George was 'No-Show Jones' for a while, then, for much of the same while, Tammy was 'Tammy Whynot'.

She had little luck with her bedfellows. Tammy, then known as Virginia Pugh, had to sleep with her grandpa till she was thirteen; after that, the bed choices were her own. Her first recorded liaison, at seventeen, with a Tornado Valley man called Euple Byrd, was full of abuse, amongst it his habit of mocking her ambitions. 'You want to be a hillbilly singer? Dream on, baby, dream on,' he told her when she bundled the kids into the car and headed out of the marriage and into Nashville. This being myth, there was little to dream about when she got there – the birth of a child with spinal meningitis, a severe depression, arrest and incarceration for unfit mother-hood, the kidnap of her kids by Euple, who was aided and abetted by her own mother, who testified in court on Euple's behalf – just the usual things. But Tammy triumphed; in a little image of her whole life, she met Euple again. It was out-side an Alabama concert-hall, ten years later, and he came up and asked for her autograph. She signed her photo with her new name, adding the inevitable envoi: 'Dream on, baby, dream on.'

Her first love in Nashville was a struggling songwriter named Don Chapel. He lasted less than a year. He foolishly invited a big Nashville name to dinner, and, according to legend, Tammy left with the other man that same night. One hopes Don got a lyric for a good ol' 'Slide off 'f your Satin Sheets' number out of it, anyway. His triumphant rival was none other than George himself, and here myth gives way to supermyth; George's wooing of Tammy puts Cleopatra's perfumed seduction of Mark Antony deep into the front-porch shade.

Jones, then the top Nashville cookie, wooed the songstress-rookie with diamond rings and limousines. They moved into a mansion – the mansion on the hill of archetype – where they had a pool built in the shape of a guitar and crystal chandeliers in the shape of wagon-wheels. Let he who is without taste cast the first stone; their car was a plain white Pontiac convertible, except for a few customized details like the fact that there were 4,000 silver dollars embedded in the dashboard. There were bull-horns fixed on the bonnet and a western saddle was wedged between the seats. The door-handles were pistols, the radio came on by pulling a trigger, and the horn, pressed, made a sound like a bull's bellow.

But Tammy's marriage ran into the period when George was quacking like a duck under the influence of ephedrine, or whatever it was, and vignettes of soirées chez les Joneses do not sound like the kind of scenes the average neighbour would want to keep up with. Tammy finally left him after he chased her round the house with a .30 rifle. She did attempt to stand by him, engaging Willie Nelson and other Nashvilleites to try to stop him drinking, but when they came up and took his cars away, he still managed to get to the bars of Broadway by drink-driving himself there on his motor-mower. So Tammy moved on. She went out with, but did not marry, Burt Reynolds. She barely went out with, but did marry – for a grand total of forty-four days – a real estate agent called Michael Tomlin. And finally, in 1978, she alighted on George Richey, who had supported her through Jones's binges. He – solid, dependable, manager as well as husband – is still with her.

But she's a fearsome woman, is our Tammy, not at all cowed by having sung 'Stand By Your Man' and, on the surface, not having followed her own instruction. When President-to-be Clinton was 'associated' with Gennifer Flowers and First Lady-to-be Hillary went on TV to assert that she was 'not some little woman staying at home and baking cookies, standing by my man like Tammy Wynette', Tammy, the First Lady of Country Music, fought back, blasting her insensitivity to 'all the little women who stand by their men', and Hillary, in a way neither pre- nor post-cedented, jumped down off her high horse and apologized. 'Women everywhere like my music,' Tammy says, 'because I sing about the ordinary things that women go through: being at home, divorce, worrying about the kids or being put down just because you're a woman. Women everywhere relate to those problems.' Even in the White House, it seems; the two First Ladies kissed and made up, and Tammy went on with her 200-gigs/ two-operations-a-year schedule.

That singer's a cunt . . .

Are C&W people sexist? Does Dolly Parton sleep on her back?

The Tartan Club, the works bar for the Scottish and Newcastle brewery on Fountainbridge in Edinburgh, sits mistily in the brewery steam, hung over with the smell of hops or malt or whatever pints of heavy are made from. Just as heavy is the air of old-time sexual politics. Inside it's charity night and the place is packed with an oddball crowd of cowboys and rockabilly fiends. Jackie, the Tucson club organizer, is run off his feet, sweating a bit and swearing a bit because the 300 or so present don't think much of the act currently on stage. The singer is an Edinburgh-born hippie-alike who, having travelled the States playing an odd country-folk crossover routine, has now come home and is trying to crack the British country scene. Listening to a singing fish out of water is not quite in the watching-paint-dry league, so the crowd aren't slow-hand-clapping yet; but there are mutterings, and the dance-floor is deserted.

I'm at a table with Steve, who fronts a Scottish C&W band, and his road manager, Willie. Steve is forty, one would think, handsome in a raffish way, steady-chinned, denim-shirted. Willie, who has a club of his own, the Silver Spur at Linwood, is a little older but looks a lot older – maybe that T-shirt is not quite the thing – but he's on form. 'Don't bother with the Opry, son. See the Opry?' (We are talking the Grand Ole Opry at Paisley Road Toll in Glasgow, not the Ryman Auditorium in Nashville.) 'The boys only go there to look for a lumber; they only go because it's cheaper than the dancing. You know something? If you canny score on a Saturday night in the Opry you're a poof,' he says. 'In fact, you can probably still score, even if you are a poof.'

Two women from England, who, he says, are Steve's biggest fans, arrive. They're not the handsomest of women but Steve is their passion. They tell tales of him on tour, how he puts a rose under his hat and selects a member of the audience, often a wheelchaired one, to present it to. They love him for that. Once on tour one of them asked for a beer-mat Steve's pint was on; he signed it – they love him for that – and it's framed now, up on the wall in the Steve nook in Jeanine's sitting-room, along with a framed crisp-packet into which Steve's guitar-picking hand once ferreted. He gave them that too, and they love him for that. They *adore* him for that. They tell tales about how they hang around the van when he's staying away, out on tour . . .

It's not Steve's fault, however; he looks a bit put out, stops to listen to the singer for a minute, surveys the uninterested crowd and says, simply, distractedly, 'That singer's a cunt.' As he speaks a woman from the rockabilly table gets up and walks by on her way to the bar. She is dressed not so much in westernwear as in underwesternwear; she wears a slippy lace top, a high-cut pair of lace hot-pants and a cowboy hat. The cowboy hat is the only thing you can't see through. 'Aye,' says Willie, 'and that cunt's a singer.'

I've never thought much of lemon-yellow myself . . .

At Rosedene, the bed and breakfast just round the corner from the Buffalo Club at Barton Cross, near Horndean, the owners are Buffalo members. Pam is a pert, pretty woman. When I get in she's at the ironing-board, sitting down, while Bob watches TV. She apologizes for not getting up. 'It's women's things,' she says. 'We just have to get them done . . .' Bob is no idler, incidentally, though what he seems to be is good with his hands. On the back of what's basically a two-bed B&B he's put in a swimming-pool and a spa. Out front there's a pretty, hacienda-style aspect; if there aren't wagon-wheels there ought to be, because there are brick arches curving alla Mexicana over the gap between his house and the next. And this is a house on Rosemary Way; the next road along is called Acacia Avenue.

It's a Dallas Palace, this Rosemary Way Southfork; and Pam does have a bit of Miss Ellie about her, Bob a touch of Jock Ewing. Inside he shows me his den. There's a guitar and an organ on which he fiddles with country songs; he paints too, watercolours and oils, landscapes, but he does that upstairs. This being the John Wayne Room, there are photos of the Duke all along one wall. It's also the gun-room, Pam says, though there are fewer guns in evidence than there are hats; in the corner there's a stand, like an oversized mug-tree, of stetsons and ten-gallon hats in blacks and browns, in leathers and suedes. But they're staying on the mug-tree tonight; they've had a busy week and aren't going to the Buffalo this weekend. I pull my boots on and wander down there, and don't get back till past twelve.

Bob has told me he'll be up, whatever time it is, and he is; he's sitting up watching a re-run of *Shaft* on a cable-channel called TNT. He is a heating engineer who retired because of a heart condition and found that down here, near the sea, he feels better. He has children, but he lost them when he left his wife for Pam and he's never seen them since. 'They take sides, you see,' he says placidly. 'It hurts at first, but you get used to it. Nothing you can do about it. So you just have to get on, you see?' It's his key phrase, and I do see, especially when he describes his definitively mucky divorce; £8,000, between the two of them, paid to lawyers to divide a diminishing pot. And so to Rosemary Way, and his building and his sitting up late.

The bed is covered in lacy pillows with little bows, and a fluffy soft-toy cat sits in the middle of the pile; it's not a bed to lie on in my cowboy boots. The room is spotless, with polished Mirrorglides along one wall, gleaming laminated chests-of-drawers with polished brass handles along another. But the male–female thing doesn't quite pan out as one would expect. Pam works. 'I like it when she goes out,' says Bob. 'It gets her out of my hair.' It's not because they're miserable; it's because he's house-proud. And when I get up for breakfast, Bob has the stripy apron on, and it's he who provides a heaving plate of sausage, bacon, egg, tomato, mushroom and – like a Nashville Shoney's – hash browns. Pam hovers as he works, and once the plates are on the table, they drift off to their lounge and divide their *Mail on Sunday*.

As I go I sign the visitors' book. Above me, there's a testimony from a young woman, a weekly boarder for the past six months, that if she had to choose between Pam and Bob and her own parents, she would choose Pam and Bob. And before I go, we chat for a bit about the C&W dress codes; how nice it is for men, in their blacks and their hats; how sickly some of the womenswear, with all the frills and lacy bits and dodgy colour-schemes. Pam's built slim enough to wear anything, I tell her, and she takes it as it's offered. She prefers trousers and a nice shirt, she says: 'I've never thought much of lemon-yellow myself.'

Dolly Parton sleeps on her front, and soundly too.

I don't get roses, I get rifles . . .

Jo wants to demonstrate the power of her gun. 'My husband got it me for our wedding anniversary; I don't get roses, I get rifles.' She takes me out into the garden to have a shot. The neighbours don't mind, or at any rate they're used to it, because she's done it for them at cosy neighbourhood fireworks parties over the years. Outside, she fires a couple of shots at the grey March skies, and then we go back in to finish our tea.

I'm back in commuter-land, a different but similar Hampshire town where people live out that precarious balance between a 'better quality of life' and the fast train to London. Jo, who has two children whom she ferries to and from school and Cubs and youth clubs, lives in a biggish modern seventies semi in a line of biggish modern seventies semis. Her cul-de-sac house, though, is called Calamity, and it's full of cowboy hats and holsters and fringed buckskin jackets as well as the toy-and-comic debris of family life. In the garden, her engineer-husband has been building a scale model of a Wild West railway – wooden bridges, tracks, passes and all – along the grass bank of the neatly trimmed lawn, and the shed – the other shed, not the one with the bikes and the spades and the lawnmower – is a western shack with a balcony and a front-porch railing you could tie your hoss to and a bottle of Jack Daniels on the sundowner tray in the cupboard.

Jo wants to take me to a new restaurant, Blazing Saddles, that's opened in the Market Square in Alton, so we walk down there; down some more Acacia Avenues of biggish seventies semis, through a small, hilly park of limited, suburban beauty, up into the pretty littleness of her pretty little town. She's dressed western for me coming, but she doesn't seem sure about whether she should have worn it out in the midday sun. 'I'm never sure whether to wear this stuff or not,' she says. 'Fringed buckskin would be my daily wear. But – well – sometimes I've threatened to pick up my daughter from school dressed like this and she says, *Mum* . . . So I don't get to wear my guns often. It's a shame. I do like a good swagger.' As we walk, even though there's barely a sideways glance at her, she turtles along self-consciously.

She has a 'handle', a western name chosen to meld with an historical alter ego. Her handle is Kitty Le Roy, and it's a pronouncedly 'Don't Call Me Babe' routine. 'I can't bear the women in western films, all that good-looking tomboy stuff. I got interested in this woman when I read about her in *Titbits*, quite a few years ago now. It said that she went about armed to the teeth, bristling with knives and guns, and I said to myself, I like this one. She lived by the gun, as they say, in Dallas in the 1880s; and she had five husbands, and the last one killed her. He outdrew her! Not on, is it? But she had outdrawn the other four, so I suppose fair's fair.' She pushes her mousy long hair back over her nice, pale face. 'I liked her because she sounded colourful. Not so long ago – after I joined this re-enactment group called the River Valley Rebels – someone rang me up and told me that she was an outlaw who could outdraw and outslug the whole population of Dallas. A red-blooded woman, I thought. Nice one.'

Blazing Saddles is quiet at midday, and while Jo goes off to say hello to her friend the chef, I take a look around. It's a checked-tablecloth sort of place with burgers and ribs on the menu, flintlocks hanging on the wall and 'Desperado' on the sound-system. There's a working pianola which comes on in the evenings, and there's a chaos of murals, flags and posters with a Southern States theme. There's 'RIP – THE SOUTHERN CONFEDERACY', '4th REGIMENT NEW HAMPSHIRE VOLUNTEERS', and – a special post-marital bit of Americana – 'THE UNION IS DISSOLVED', facsimiled from the *Charleston Mercury Gazette*. The chef is not in, so Jo returns alone. Is she worried about what her daughter takes from her mother having so red-blooded an idol? 'I hope that she's getting to an age when she can appreciate the difference between reality bad and fantasy bad; that fantasy bad adds colour, as long as you can appreciate the difference. The main thing is that I try to communicate to Sam the idea that women shouldn't have a passive role; and she does get very cross when people talk about women in the past and what they did and what they didn't do. In that way she's more of a feminist than I am, and I'm glad.'

Jo's own life has had enough reality bad in it, anyway; her conversation is peppered with references to a bad bout of post-natal depression when Sam was born. 'Stand By Your Man' comes on the stereo, as it happens, but it sounds like it was the other way round for a bit, that Gra, her husband – Jack Coltrane to her Kitty Le Roy – stood by her and helped her through. Her voice still has a shakenness, her laugh a nervousness, like life was scary for a bit; but her middle-class world safety-netted her while the western world was a therapy and an escape, something which she and her husband took up together but something in which he participates principally for her sake. 'He likes to be a gunslinger in black, but don't they all, these men? It's all right for them, with all those choices, all those roles – you know, they have that option of "Think I'll be a marshal or a mountain-man or a gold-digger today." But I'm a bit stuck. I don't want to be a saloon-girl. And I can't be a cowgirl – I don't know anything about cows. And I don't know one end of a horse from the other.

'But I am interested in what women did do, or could do. Long ago – years ago – I got fascinated by the idea of the west; you see the guns, you see the bravado, and it fascinated me, I don't know why. When I was at school I watched *Butch Cassidy and the Sundance Kid*, and I started having a sort of fantasy about a woman being in Robert Redford's place; and ever since I've been writing this sort of novel about this person, about this woman character. Basically I put her into the Wild West world, and she wears all the garb, you know, and she goes out rooting, tooting and shooting. She's been an outlaw, and she ends up a deputy sheriff; she ends up a mayor, and running her own ranch. Blimey!' she calls girlishly. 'If I met her in the High Street I'd probably run a mile . . .'

Coffee comes, and we sip; I light a cigarette, an act that makes me feel a little outré in this company. 'It takes place in Montana, in the latter half of the nineteenth century, but the heroine's a bit ahead of the game. A bit like Calamity Jane, only worse; well, Calamity Jane never interested me, because you have that tomboy look, but you never really know what's going on inside there, do you? But my woman, well – she's bisexual, and people don't accept her. Women in the west – well, they were feisty. My woman has kids, sure, by a cowhand who gets killed, and she has a male lover later on. But her best friend is a girl with whom' – Jo squelches her lips cunnilingually – 'she has a quick canoodle every now and then. The friend gets raped and she thinks her brother is murdered by the rapists after a bank robbery, so she kills the leader after a gun fight. You know the way – sex, blood and gore. Raunchy. You know, I can't show the kids . . .'

We walk up, retracing our steps, up through the town and back to the concrete greys of her street. 'I should say I'm not like that . . . I've an ordinary life, really, and I love men. But there you go. I thought I'd probably never finish it, but lo and behold, I *have* finished it; and I think it'll never be published in my entire life, but at least I've done it. It's taken eleven years, what with the kids and the depression and all the work at home, that meant that I couldn't work for a while.' We stand by the door – it's a nice bit of mock-Georgian, of course, with a bell-shaped knocker – and she prepares to go back to making some order out of Calamity. 'The title? Well, the title was *A Rancher's Daughter*, but I thought that was a bit tame, considering everything that was going on. After a bit of thought Gra came up with *No Ordinary Girl*, which I quite liked. It doesn't sound too bad, does it? Though I'm thinking of *No Ordinary Woman . . .*'

You only live once. And you're a long time dead . . .

Let me call the couple this tale tells of Harry and Sally, and let me say only that they are a well-known couple in the C&W world of one of the provinces of the British Isles. Of their identities there will be few more clues, and such as there are will be accidental. As far as Harry goes, this subterfuge is of no real significance. His situation is clear and no one in his life is deceived. But Sally, for reasons that will become very clear, is unwilling to have her identity, and her life, blown open. It's hardly a case of protecting the innocent – Sally has a laugh on her that is jolly-evil to her joyful-wanton heart – but it is a case of protecting her back and her meal-ticket and the shape of her life.

I'm sitting in a works club in a heavy industrial zone in their town. I've arranged to meet Sally there. She's about forty-odd, Sally; quite short, stout in a fit, line-danced sort of way, with a keen, intent face, full of hospitality and care for my well-being;

though I've only chatted on the phone with her and though she doesn't know me from Grandpa Jones, she's all apology that I have to use a bed and breakfast, that she doesn't offer me a bed at her house. Within a minute of meeting me she's telling me, as if she knew me, that if she'd known me there would have been no problem. Harry is sitting with her when I arrive and she introduces me to him as 'another member of my club'. The club may as well have a changed name too; we'll call it the Tombstone, though Sally's tale suggests she's avoided an early grave rather than stepped into one. While Sally's in standard frilly blouse and dancing-skirt, Harry's positively stylish; he's wearing an elegant blue-and-white western shirt and an off-white stetson with a rakish feather. He dances too, though he looks less fit; with a vodka and Coke in him his face reddens up, as his type of face does; not unhandsome, it has a bit of Dickie Davies in it, but flushed, it has a bit of Rab C. Nesbitt in it too.

Foolish at first, I ask Sally about her husband, but all she'll say is that he's not interested in all this stuff. And then the hints start falling, heavy as sequoia trees. 'I'm out every night,' she says, 'dancing, out with these friends, in the country music world.' Innocuous enough, but then I describe someone I know who's marrying for a second time. 'I bet they're happier this time round,' she says earnestly, and her face turns to watch the dancers dancing to a Nanci Griffith number. Harry flashes her a big, beaming smile and they get up on to the floor. At first it's a quickish waltz, then a quick line-dance number, and then it's a full-scale smoochie ('Islands in the Stream', that is what they are) that makes them look anything but fellow-members of the same committee; or, if they are so, it's a committee I wouldn't mind being on once in a while, as, as they part, he looks in her eyes and she twirls her skirt.

They come back and, in concert, tell me a story about being on one of the Pontin's weekend festivals. 'See that woman there?' Sally starts. 'She was in the next chalet to us. And about three o'clock in the morning –' She giggles. 'About three o'clock in the morning,' Harry continues, 'we'd come in from the dance, and all we hear are these noises, coming through the walls.' He starts moaning his way through a Hollywood orgasm, until the laugh obstructs the sigh: 'Mmmmm, Mmmmm, Mmmmm, Mmmmergh –' 'Next morning we get up,' says Sally, 'and we says to her, "Oh-oh, what was going on in there?" I say to her, "What in God's name were *you* up to last night?" And she says, "Sally," she says, "I was washing my feet. Having a bath. After all that dancing –" And we'd been lying there together listening to –' She stops, realizing that the game, or the barest fraction of the rules of the game that were left, is given away. The precise level of their compadritude is on the table, even if, for the moment, everyone's too polite to pick it up.

The next night, at a small C&W club in a small cricket club pavilion in a small town not far from where they live, we meet up again. The atmosphere's different from the off. (I tell Harry I've spent the afternoon lying in my hotel bed watching the rugby on television, and he asks, with a leer, 'How many balls were in that game, then?') It's clear that they've agreed that I'm okay, that they can talk. For Harry, as I say, there's no problem, though his ménage is a bit unusual. His wife is with him but not with him. She left him a few years back; once a week she would take the handicapped kids she worked with on a bus trip, and, finding her life too stationary for her liking, she ran off with the coach-driver. But he died of cancer and his council house was lost, so rather than leaving her out on the street, Harry let her come back to live in their married home. 'It's separate rooms and separate lives,' he says. 'She knows and doesn't know what goes on. We've worked it all out.'

'It's all right for him,' says Sally. For her it's not so easy, this 'Daytime Friends and Night-time Lovers' routine. She has a husband at home and a grown-up daughter-with-child at home and neither of them knows how her life has shaped up. She draws a picture of a classically hollow marriage, here in this grey granite town. Her husband of seventeen years is a fireman, permanently on shifts, permanently tired. 'At times when I've had a job, maybe a nine-to-five job, well, as he came in in the morning, I'd be going out, and as I came in at night he'd be going out to work.' More importantly, there's a complete divergence of interests. A dour man with a liking for a game of billiards, he is not interested in C&W or dancing or cowboys. She is obsessed, especially with the cowboy bit; or especially, as Harry might twinkily have said, with the bits of a cowboy. Love is in the air, of that there's no doubt, and it's the kind of love that infuses everything, that inflates all the sagging parts of one's existence; that smiles the face, that springs the step, that hits right on the button.

And so Sally lives a life which negates the negative and accentuates the positive; everything is shaped and sorted to keep her from the death-in-life her marriage was bringing her to. 'Yes,' she says. 'Every night I'm out the door, up the garden path, on the way out; Cinderella's going to the ball. Cinderella comes to the ball, and dances, and talks, and has a good time. And everyone sees Cinderella leave the club at half-eleven; but that doesn't mean Cinderella gets home at midnight . . .' Her laugh is full-scale dirty, solidly in touch with herself. The secrecy doesn't bother her, though occasionally the whole thing, the whole pattern, makes her strain in pain: 'The only time I ever get depressed is when I'm on my way back up that garden path, and I get in, and the house is clean and tidy – I do everything right, you see – but when I walk in the door, I know I don't really live there; I live out here. But you know something? I've got more night-time clothes than daytime clothes; I've more dressing-up clothes than normal clothes. I live on Fantasy Island.'

They're not like any adulterers I've ever met. What makes the difference, it seems, is the freedom they appear to have; they're guiltless, because within the C&W world they're more or less free to behave as they want. They've had the odd panic when TV cameras, in search of the visual gag cowboys offer, have turned up to film for local news. ('It's not my husband – he doesn't watch. But I've a neighbour who sits there until that wee white dot appears.') When they're on their bus trips or their days out they ham it up; they do turns together, as a couple, when they go to Pontin's or when their club has a day or a night out. Their latest act has Sally handcuffing Harry to a chair and, dominatrix-like, standing over him as he pleads, in song, 'Please Release Me . . .' For someone whose life was so close to emotional imprisonment, it seems a risqué number, but she thinks it's the funniest thing she's ever heard. 'You only live once,' she says, without a flicker of profundity, 'and you're a long time dead.'

I wish you don't do like I do . . .

Maybe Sally equals Ruby just as x equals o; I don't know. Sally's tale, of course, clogs me to some degree, fills me with paranoia that I am just a billiard-playing fireman at heart. It also releases me, fills me with a small sense that the right outcome has happened, since nobody human could wish to see a woman's life fade, as Sally's might have done, as Ruby says hers was doing before she decided to take her love to town; she has told me again and again (she's not at all sure that I've listened) of her unspeakable loneliness in our relationship, and tonight, in the town where I am but which I'm not mentioning, I'm glad for her. It happens from time to time; good will breaks out against my will. If she's out, she's out, I think; good luck to her: *I wish you love and happiness/ I guess I wish you all the best . . .*

But nothing is as benevolent as a wish for love and happiness in the topsy-turvy honky-tonk world of marital breakdown, and as the months go by it's clear that Ruby's world is not as simple as Sally's. Sometimes it's hard to be a woman, and while a man opting to live apart from his children is likely to be viewed tolerantly – i.e. as a shit, but only as much of a shit as can be expected – a woman opting to do so is greeted with at best bewilderment and at worst a friends-and-familial lynch-mob. In the early months, the forces of light line up to give the forces of darkness a hard time; Ruby is made a stranger at the threshold by more people than it is possible to count, and in her own family there is a great deal of talk about 'abandonment' and 'desertion'. And though like a good new man I try, the bit of me that still stings with resentment has a hard time not agreeing with the old men: *I wish you don't do like I do / And ever fall in love with someone like you . . .*

Willie Nelson once made an album about divorce in which side A is the man's perception of things and side B is the woman's. (It was what we used to call, unhumorously, a concept album, as if all other albums were just put together raggle-taggly and cotton-tailed.) What follows should be taken with a proper dose of the side B-ness of things; but as things unfold, I begin to feel that Ruby is her own worst enemy.

I try saying to her that she should bask in the knowledge of the right thing done, that she should be happy; but she cannot quite accept the parameters of her actions, and she insists again and again that her departure was not the precipitate action of someone gripped by passion, but an act of generosity; by leaving, she says, she has spared us a lot of conflict, and she insists again and again that I, and the world, should be grateful. Meanwhile, the Greek is proving to be a difficult character/man of integrity (delete as applicable) who, it seems, is not prepared to play a social game and smile and seem what he is not in the period it would take for people to adjust. Quickly Ruby and he start to play a dangerous who's-not-with-us-is-against-us game; they cut off friends and family who do not show unilateral support, and since, as I say, I have already gathered around me legions of fawning and one-sided supporters, she is left with few outlets for contact with the world beyond the bed she's made for herself and in which she lies with him.

Soon it becomes clear that all's not as it should be. If she's so happy, I think, why does her mind continually turn to what's no longer hers? The family house she's left becomes the focus for her discontent; she believes that she should be able to come and go as she chooses. I feel that by normal standards I'm reasonable (I don't object, for instance, to the Greek coming round and hanging out while she's babysitting for me), but when I suggest that her overall attitude (her flat is hers, my house is ours) is a tad unrealistic, she accuses me of becoming proprietorial, of being exclusive, of not recognizing her place in the family, of seeking to take control of everything, of wishing to shut her out. Which crime, of course, to some extent, I admit (in fact I wish only to murder her, not to shut her out), but to which I am common-sensical defensical: if you start shagging someone else and move in with them, don't you expect to find yourself a mite outside the bosom of the family?

There are many famous revenge stories associated with jilted lovers – the grass seed planted in the carpet and watered in high summer; the prawns stuffed and left to rot and smell, undetectable inside the roller of the roller-blind; the tale of Lady Whatsername who ran round the village handing out her husband's connoisseur collection of fine wines. In all these cases, the jilted seeks to take revenge on the jiltee, the cuckold on the cuckolder. But I find myself in a much more bizarre position, in which whatever's going on between Ruby and the Greek gets taken out on me. Feeling that *I* am neglectful of *them*, they embark on what I come to think of as a policy of terrorism designed to discomfit me – the one they've cuckolded – as much as possible. I think they're responding to jealousy and paranoia; they think they're making me see how things have been for them. They want to teach me a lesson; to teach me – as Robert de Niro says with appropriate melodrama in *Cape Fear* – the meaning of loss.

It starts with the house, and then it spreads. In terms of the house, the main tactic is this; whenever I've said or done something they think I shouldn't, they, or more usually she, comes round and sets up camp; she brings a duvet-cover and a set of pillow-cases and makes up the spare-room bed. She claims she's moving back in to assert her rights; of course what she's banking on is that I'll get pissed off and that she can therefore make some difference to my life. When I de-make the spare-room bed she makes it again, and when I de-make the spare-room bed again she makes it again, and when I de-make the spare-room bed a third time (she always complained that I had more stamina than her) she retreats. But she only retreats as far as my room where, gold marker in hand, she scribbles on the walls. RUDE, she writes in big letters on one wall, then RUDE, in big letters on another wall, then ILL-MANNERED, in big letters on the third wall, then – clearly running out of synonyms – she returns to RUDE on the fourth.

There's another incursion, too. One holiday I go off travelling; the children are, I think, at Ruby's flat. I return to find that the Greek and she have basically moved into the house for a week. I object, not so much as to their being there, as to the lack of courtesy. (This house is my home, but also my office, the centre of my existence.) I object fairly straightforwardly, and receive a chill response through the mail, a letter that says that the house would have been sold were there no children, *ergo* the house is the children's house, *ergo* as the children's mother she has a right to come and go as she pleases, *ergo* she has the right to invite anyone else she pleases to come and go likewise. The house, in other words, has no connection to me; I am merely an adjunct who happens to live with the children.

The logic is indisputable; not that that stops me disputing it. My response is an eight-page fax, ringing with righteous denunciation, blooming with rhetoric too embarrassingly florid to quote here. Suffice it to say that only on page eight do I get round to saying what I mean, and it can be summarized in not much more than eight words: that what she's saying is bollocks, and that she has to accept the consequences of leaving. My letter does not go down well, and although I've 'established' that I need to be informed if the Greek is coming to the house, he turns up, unannounced, next time she comes round, and forces his way in. It's a bit of tomcattery, and, righteous and defensive, I have no compunction in spraying the borders of my territory freely. I say quietly that I won't fight him with the children in the house and ask him to leave. He tells me to fuck off. I ask him again, even more quietly, and tell him that if he doesn't leave I will call the police. He tells me to fuck off. I dial 999. (Neither of us is touched with imaginative genius at this moment of supremely typical post-maritalism.) The rozzers don't come, but advise him on the phone to leave, and they both do, smashing the hinges of the gate in their rage.

Later they return, after the children are asleep. In they bundle, Ruby in shock, the Greek bristling. As Ruby sits on the stairs, haunted and silent, he tells me what he thinks of me. Reader, I confess: I am a motherfucker (thirty-six times over), a cunt (fifty-one times over), a wanker (innumerable, like the number of pancakes Black Sambo ate). After about an hour of staying silent I start laughing, which brings me wagging-finger rebukes. The finger goes to my eye, and he tells me I am finished if I do something or other again. I say, 'It's funny how often I'm told these things, how rarely anything happens.' He says that if I do whatever-it-is again I'm finished; I say that it's funny how often I'm told these things and how rarely anything happens. And, of course, nothing does. The washing-machine controls revolve, and we're in the repeat cycle, on and on till rage is washed out, till the duvet-covers have sufficient times come on and off our emotional beds.

For some reason they then decide to turn their attention to more trivial annoyances, and the camper-van becomes the focus of their *jihad*. Even though Ruby has verbally passed it on to me, she has kept the spare keys, and she begins to remove it from its parking-place without telling me. The first time I find it at her flat, with a chain round the steering-wheel; it's returned when I'm adjudged to have learned my lesson. The next time, the same; it goes round the corner and stays for a few days while I stew and plead. Then up a step; it is driven to the other side of town. The trick is to tell me where it is but not to tell me that the alarm is on (she's whipped the controls from my underpants drawer). I get in and the siren starts. Reckless, I drive it through town (cars ahead of me, thinking I'm an ambulance, move to the side of the road to let me through) and hot-wheel it into the car-park of her flats. She's embarrassed, so next time she just krookloks it in my driveway (quieter). When that fails (any second-class burglar knows how to get one of those off, and the bloke at the local DIY, a divorcé himself, is happy to help) she drives it away and leaves it in a village miles away, where I find it only because it gets reported to the police as causing an obstruction.

It sounds like nothing; maybe it is nothing, except days, endless days, spent looking for the thing or negotiating with people power-crazy/ distraught (delete as applicable) enough to believe that such things change things, any more than things are changed by negotiation itself. The sad thing is that while she believes that these actions will make me have respect for her, they in fact leave me without any capacity for sympathy. My fault, maybe: but from now on, whenever I'm told Ruby is missing the children, it – like Biko's death was supposed to do to the South African Home Secretary – leaves me cold. They also make me aware how vulnerable my back is. With some regret I make an appointment with a solicitor and, searching for clarification, begin to sue for divorce.

Some turn to drink, some to drugs. I wrote my way out of it . . .

I have to say – in case it isn't obvious already – that my interest in Tammy Wynette started as a bit of a joke. To the non-C&W ear Tammy is everything that's wrong with C&W – her stuff is

steel-guitar-twangy, key-change-sentimental, politically oppro-
brious. Look at 'Stand By Your Man', her great standard. There's
the opening, with the choking voice made faintly ridiculous by
the Alabam' accentuation (*So-ometimes it's hawuurd to be a
wumman, givin' all your luuuve to just one mu-yan*). There's
the little tremolo of we-women-know painedness (*You'll ha-uy-ve
a bad time*), and the acceptance that *He'll have a good time/
doing things that you don't understand* followed by – worse,
politically, that *If you love him, you'll forgive him . . . for, after
all, he's just a man.* And then the pedal steel winds up for that
big *BLAM BLAM BLAM – STAND BY YOUR MAN . . .*

Get beyond 'Stand By Your Man' and you come across a whole
range of weepies, like 'D-I-V-O-R-C-E' (featuring the *de rigueur*
trademark key-change on the second verse as we're told to watch
the sprog smile because he thu-uh-unks it's Christmas) and, of
course, 'I Don't Want to Play House', in which a mother overhears
a couple of toddlers declining to play such a game because it
makes her momma cry because when mommy and daddy played
it her daddy said goodbye. Buoyed by the humour, I listened to
her for a bit, collecting *bons mots*; for a while 'Kids Say the
Darnedest Things' was my favourite. But then, sure enough, I
began to go native; began to get offended at people laughing at
her; began to find myself defending her; began to realize that
something in that voice had begun to speak to me. But it wasn't
until I met Debra that I realized what it was.

In the front room of Debra's house in Clacton-on-Sea the
bookshelves are lined with Tammy Wynette videos with dra-
matic I-have-suffered titles like 'Tears of Fire'. There's some
George Jones there, some Conway Twitty, and – the favourites
of Debra's second husband, a long-distance trucker – some
rougher, honky-tonk stuff by Tom T. Hall and some Bobby Bare.
But Tammy is the real McCoy, as far as Debra's concerned. She
has just been to see Tammy and George play a 'Together Again'
show in London, where eleven years before she'd been a victim
of No-Show Jones no-showing at Wembley. Of course Tammy

showed, way back then, just as she would now, and, back then, Debra got backstage. In the picture she has of Tammy with herself, Tammy looks just like she always does; Debra looks like a sparrow, tiny and thin, with a face that's clear and happy. She's smart in a dress that leaves her shoulders bare, and Tammy's hand is round her. Debra has the broad, dimply smile of a child. Her slight squint changes nothing; she looks clear ahead, straight as an arrow.

Here, in her house, a decade later, she has a child with her, her son, an eighteen-monther in a red romper, one of those indestructible lumps of funny, fearless flesh that cruises rooms bumping, crashing and prying into everything. Debra doesn't find it funny. She shows me some of his things. He has a rocking-horse with a saddle, a cowboy hat, a pistol-packing dolly and his own guitar. She does smile at these things, and, as it happens, she stands in front of the picture of herself with Tammy c. 1985. It's a weird moment; she holds the doll, and you can see in her whole carriage that she's fully grown now, yet fully diminished. She's still thin, but now her thinness looks like weight lost, and her skin no longer has a translucent shine. She wears a short dowdy sweater and a pair of moccasins, and her house – a low, grey bungalow, miles from the sea, on the way out of town – has the same air of like-it-or-lump-it. There's a stuffy smell, a blocked Ventaxia, brown rings round the inside of the coffee-cup, a look in her eyes that makes you feel she'll never look at you.

Yet she looks at her life in a way that's relentless, and the things that have happened in it are not what Tammy would call 'the ordinary things that women go through'. Up on the TV is a picture of another child, Jessie, in whose bright smile you see the same clear face that Tammy longs to be close to in the picture, and the dizzying confusion I feel as my eye revolves – Debra with Tammy, Jessie with Debra, Debra with husband – shakes me up. Jessie – Jessie Alethea Kara, a name plucked from a Dottie West number – is Debra's lost child. She is eight now, living somewhere in Essex or in a neighbouring county, with contact restricted by Social Services' adoption policy to a school photograph and a Christmas card once a year. Lost to her natural mother and her birth-story, she sounds like a teenage heartache waiting to happen.

Debra went into a post-natal psychosis when Jessie was born. She went to the doctor, who failed her miserably: 'Men don't understand,' she says, 'and the doctor just didn't know. He just kept going on about "changes" and "a new life". Told me to "pull myself together".' So she tried. First she tried staying put, braving it out; and when that didn't cure her longing to be away from her husband and the baby, she left her child with the husband – her first husband, this was – and went off for five weeks. 'Well, he was a better father than I was a mother,' she says. 'At that time anyway.' But she has already mentioned the fact that her husband was ill, and now she clarifies; her first husband was a schizophrenic, whose condition was drug-controlled. Social Services didn't rate the husband's care. 'They came along and interfered. They basically tricked us into having Jessie taken into voluntary care. First for a month, then for three months – "For Jessie's own protection," they said – and we cooperated because we loved her and we thought we had nothing to hide; we'd asked for help because we thought that if we were open with them they'd be open with us.'

She has the set expression of someone to whom nothing worse can happen; her voice doesn't break, there is no hysteria, no taut-lipped repression. She completes the tale quickly, in a quiet, unrushed way: at the end of the three months, the Social Services took the case to court to apply for an adoption order. No ordinary things, but an ordinary woman: 'It was so confusing. All these reports,' she says in a flat, still voice, barely rising above a revved Capri on the grey asphalt outside. 'By the end it was so hard to say – out of all the stuff that was going on in my head – it was so hard to say what was post-natal depression and what was something else. But I knew I wanted her back.'

But meanwhile, of course, as the process dragged on, Jessie was being 'weaned off'; was being taken away, regardless of what Debra wanted.

The turning-point in court has echoes of Tammy which Debra claims not to have recognized; for Debra's mother, like Tammy's, stood up in court and opined that Debra was an unfit mother, that Jessie would be better off in someone else's care. No doubt she had her reasons, says Debra; no doubt she must have felt that she was doing what she had to do for the sake of her granddaughter. Still, I can't quite handle Debra's blitheness about it: 'Like a fool, you forgive her,' she says, and for a moment her matter-of-factuality makes me believe that I'm not equipped for this world, for this life. 'The family never liked my first husband, so there was something there for everyone to deal with. And then – with what happened to my husband, in the end – well, that left me with the feeling that she – my mother – wouldn't always be here. And I knew what happens; that if someone passes away and you've not been able to talk to them, for whatever reason, then you're left with so many things to say, and they break your heart, sort of . . .'

The loss of a daughter, the near-loss of a mother; the loss of a husband too. If the decencies are parcelled out unequally at birth, then the heartaches are too. In the midst of the court business Debra's schizoid husband turned up at his doctor's and declared that he was feeling well, clear-headed – 'sorted'. The doctor said that he could come off his medication if he wanted. He did, but ended up in hospital just a few weeks later. There, without the medication he needed to keep his warring sides apart, he committed suicide. Another day, another court appearance. 'He never left a note, so they made it an open verdict,' says Debra. 'But I knew . . .' She knew – she knew lots of things – and to cope, she 'shut the world out' and began to write songs, country songs. 'Some turn to drink, some to drugs. But I wrote my way out of it.'

She produces a tape. She won't play it for me there and then, but I can take it away with me. It seems pretty clear that she wants me out, so I take my jacket. On the doorstep I ask about her plans: she and her husband would like to move west; get out of Clacton; maybe go down to Weymouth; somewhere warmer, as soon as the winter ends or her husband can find work. Here, in spite of the neighbour's house being called Sunnyholme, it's a grey, drizzly day; and grey, drizzly days at the seaside are greyer and drizzlier than anywhere else. Four boys in black Harringtons are having a loutish game of football at the corner and men are unloading things from hatchbacks. The idea of being west – of following the setting sun – has never been more attractive. Here there's no dream of Sierra Nevada to chase; there are just Sierras, lines and lines of them; this is the east country.

The tape is not promising; it's been copied a few times and it hisses. Some local musicians have taken the songs and arranged them and performed them, and the quality is, to say the least, variable. At times the songs are sentimental (*those big brown eyes could melt a heart of stone . . .*) and at times glib, if lyrically neat:

> *Tammy, my woman says that she is leaving home*
> *I don't want her to want a D-I-V-O-R-C-E*
> *So Tammy please sing for her* Stand By Your Man
> *Sing her out of leaving me alone . . .*

But at the centre of it is a song that, literally and unexpectedly, makes me shiver. Who knows if that moment can be communicated on paper? All I know is that the backing did it few favours; that there was awkward phrasing and untimely piano and all the other trappings of amateurism. And yet:

> *If only she hadn't been exactly what I'd always wanted*
> *This might have been a little easier*
> *I might have been able to let her go*
> *If only she hadn't been her . . .*

All the way home – along 200 miles of asphalt – I can't push the idea from my head – *If only she hadn't been her*. And I realize that what I feel doesn't come from the story, doesn't come from Debra's front room; I imagine Debra sitting, for years, staring at that photo on the TV, wishing the child had been someone else, something less beautiful, less cared for; wishing, in the end, that Debra had not been Debra.

And if you listen again to Tammy singing 'Stand By Your Man', and imagine a woman believing her schizophrenic husband to be a better parent than she, and a woman forgiving her mother's betrayal for fear of non-communication stretching to the grave, then you have something of what it's like for a deeply multiple-married Christian weepie-merchant to sing a song like that. And you realize in that moment that what speaks in Tammy's voice is sincerity, the sincerity which, over the years, C&W has had its head beaten with but which is actually its key ingredient. When a plain song becomes illuminated with feeling in that pure way, then there is nothing to beat it, and country music does that better than any other sort; better even than the blues. Suddenly, that shift of key into the second verse of 'D-I-V-O-R-C-E' sounds not only virtuosic, but uplifting too.

Take me with you, Tammy. You and Debra know what suffering is. In Ruby's case I'm not so sure, in spite of the histrionics. In my own, I know something for sure; I've nothing to complain about when others' suffering is so limitless; there's a horizon ahead of me, and it's straight and solid, and over the other side is a gleam of better days.

CHAPTER FOUR

Ain't It Good to be on the Road Again

A wife is for life . . .

I've come a long way, but I'm not quite there yet; I am not yet quite at the point where I can easily admit the ways in which I contributed to the downfall of my marriage. But I have to say that on one front – my lamentable habit of breaking into song at every possible opportunity – the evidence is overwhelming, and I have to beat my breast. Yet if only Ruby had known how much worse it could have been. 'Folsom Prison Blues' was my invariable choice of country song when I picked up my guitar when I was married, and it's not a bad song. But my repertoire has increased dramatically since then. 'Ruby, Don't Take Your Love to Town' and many others came later, in my maritally unplugged years.

The status of 'Folsom Prison Blues' was confirmed just before Ruby left. We were on our last legs and I'd tried everything; I'd tried intervening, laying off, being calm, being impassioned, and I was feeling depressed, all tried out. But there was time for one last, unusual throw of the dice at a friend's wedding. At the end of the evening the Cajun band which was playing swapped instruments and, for fun, played a trad country set – 'Jambalaya', 'Apartment Number 9', 'Hey, Good Lookin''. When the singer announced 'Folsom Prison Blues' I – for some reason I can't even now fathom – shouted, from the back, 'I'll sing!' And I did; entirely out of character, not entirely out of tune, I stood up there in front of a hundred guests and gave it laldie.

It was a rare and unexpected moment of success; or at least surprise, for Ruby. It made her pause for thought in a way no other strategy from my futile collection had done, and must have extended the life of my marriage by at least three weeks. For I was walking with a swagger, and perhaps she had another look; though in the end she would have noticed that it was a jail-song, not a love-song that I sang; that even standing on the marital fault-line I sang to the crowd, not to her. So she left anyway. But the buzz stayed with me, and I think I did understand for a while what it was like to sing for a living, and how hard it is to be sincere.

I had tried to take up writing country songs, but the hook-lines always escaped me. That is, until Ruby left; upon which event I became comparatively prolific. That's to say that I managed to come up with the chorus of one more sentimental tear-jerker than I'd ever managed before. Tailored to speak to the departing lover, I decided it would have a Tammy Wynette-esque intensity: *A wife is for life/ Not just for Christmas*, it would run, and it could've been a contender, but it never made the country charts. Since I've never finished writing it – not even after spending time on the road with a load of Britain's brightest and best country singers – I guess that's not surprising.

Sometimes he goes as far as Gilberdyke . . .

John the painter's wife's family are westerners, he says; somewhat to his embarrassment. 'I don't call them my in-laws; I call them my out-laws,' he says of Ray and Joy. He tells me that Ray doesn't like to wear his gun in the street. 'He carries it in a Grandways bag,' he adds with a wicked laugh. He tells me that Ray and Joy travel all over Hull following a local singer. 'They go and see him three, four times a week,' he says. 'He's a joiner by trade; they call him the Singing 'ammer. Barry Johns is his name.'

Barry plays Wednesdays at the Victoria Tavern, at the heart of the old Hull docks. The docks are not what they were; the banana-boats, like the L&N Railroad, don't stop here any more, and the forces of the Halfords-B&Q-Powerhouse axis are creeping up on them, retail 'park' planning permissions in hand. The pub, stranded between semi-derelict warehouses, can't do much more than scrape a living, and the management must be glad that once a week Barry brings along Ray and Joy and the twenty-odd friends who make up the Dixie Gamblers. (The Gamblers are appropriately dressed the Wednesday I show up, in black hats, long bow-ties and frilly evening-shirts.) I go along with Ian, the best gas-man in Hull, who's been on jobs with Barry before now: 'I've seen him hang a door,' he says, 'but I've never heard him sing a song.'

The Gamblers are devoted. Along the back wall of the narrow lounge, paper bunting-clad courtesy of Labatt's, there are three women who are near-identical. They have frilly skirts, lacy tops with puffed sleeves, black velvet chokers, big-lensed specs and short-cut hair permed tight; they're bright, smiley-looking women, the sort who have packets of fags stored in a leather purse along with a smart gold lighter. I ask if they're fans of Barry's and the middle one, the queen one, says, 'I ought to be; I'm his mother.' Undeterred, I go on: 'Do you follow him everywhere?' 'Everywhere.' A list of pubs follows. 'Victoria Tavern Wednesdays, Victoria Saloon Sundays . . .' 'Are they all in Hull, then, the places where he plays?' An outraged look. 'Oh no . . . sometimes he goes as far as Gilberdyke . . .'

Barry starts his set. He's a squat man, powerfully built, a smiler in a pink Ben Sherman shirt (open-necked to let a broad gold chain show) and a pair of black easy-press trousers. For a troubadour who doesn't troub any further than Gilberdyke – it's about ten miles down the road, on the road to Goole – he sure can sing a wandering-star number. His first song tells us that he's on the run and the highway is his home; his second laments the fact that when you leave you can never go back, and asks – plaintively – why he ever started to run. His third – following a gag about how his bald patch is showing – asks that his body be sent back home after he dies, and in his fourth, he wants to know what he wouldn't give to see his mummy and daddy. And while I can't speak for his daddy, I can tell him, if he really wants to know, that his mummy is sitting right opposite me and she's singing along.

Ray, John's out-law, is full of traveller's tales too. He's been to Nashville, and though it was two years back, Music City experiences still trip off his thrilled tongue; he tells me about one night, how he went to the Opry and then – alone, as Joy was ill – ventured out late to take in the Midnite Jamboree at Ernest Tubb's Record Store. Ray is a cabbie now, but he used to work the fishing-boats out of Hull docks. His country grounding occurred up in the far north fishing-grounds, off Greenland and Iceland, where American Forces' Network was all they could get on the wireless; with so many southern boys in the army, AFN played a lot of C&W. I like the sound of this, the image of a crackling signal bringing Hank or George wailing across the wild sea to a lonely crew huddled in the galley of a weather-tossed trawler; it's like Neil Armstrong listening to Tammy Wynette in space.

When Ray's boat landed in Newfoundland he'd take his pay and buy records unavailable in this country. It was the start of a big collection. 'You've seen my cabinets, haven't you?' he says to Ian. Ian nods. 'I worked out the other day,' Ray says, 'that if I started playing all my records now, and played them non-stop till I was a hundred, I'd still not get through them all.' Ian says he can believe it; and when Ray's gone, he says, 'He may look soft. But if he spent twenty years on the boats then he's a hard man. That's a hard life.' And he tells me how, like someone from a mining village who refuses to risk his life searching for the black diamonds, joining the fleet was the one thing *he* wouldn't do when he left school; that he was haunted by the sight of the boats coming back a man short.

Ray may have records by every country artiste who ever recorded, and Barry sings them on the same scattershot principle. He unships a few crateloads of love-songs. There's 'Luckenbach, Texas', that nice Waylon one about going back to the basics of love; when Barry's mum sees me singing along she's over the moon. There's 'Wind Beneath My Wings' and 'I Believe in Love'; and there's one called 'Does My Ring Hurt Your Finger?' which reduces Ian to hysterics, for while he's not a fan of Charley Pride, he's a big double-entendre buff. But taking the biscuit in the second set is 'Old Flames (Can't Hold a Candle to You)'; for on cue at the start of the chorus, out of the women's handbags come not the gold lighters, but specially bought electric candles which Barry's fans wave, swaying in time along the naugahyde benches. 'You have to admit he's a crowd-pleaser,' says Ray. I admit it, without pointing out that the crowd is practically his family.

I talk to Barry at the bar during his break. He's happy to talk, but not desperate; he tells me a few bits and pieces, but you can see he doesn't need recognition from the likes of me to make his life complete. How it started? He had an uncle who used to play him country records no one else was allowed to touch. Was he straight on to the Hull circuit when he left school? No, he moved away to the north-east, to Yarm, and he played in the pubs there until his marriage ran out. Did the music help him through that time? No, when he moved back he moved in with another woman; that helped him, and she's with him now; she doesn't mind his six-gigs-a-week schedule. Has he always been solo? No, he played in a duo called the Blue Ridge Boys with his mate Phil, but Phil went over to pop-cabaret while he remained a true believer. In fact, he says, fobbing me off, there's Phil there, at the bar. Why don't you have a word with him? I can hardly not, now; Phil, his face thin and keen where Barry's is broad and complacent, is looking at me expectantly; and in any case Barry has turned away to talk to someone more interesting.

There's no room to dance in the Vicky Tavern; but there is room for Barry's fans to practise a well-rehearsed set of routines when he takes the stage again. They perform, for instance, a series of elaborate hand-jives. When Barry sings 'The Gambler' I watch Ray's hands deal a hand of imaginary cards, fold them up, and count the imaginary winnings. When Barry does 'Friends in Low Places' the Gamblers stand up and surround the stage; they point to the floor, they throw back a whisky, they swill a beer-chaser. Then, on another number I don't recognize, the whole cowboy crew inexplicably gets up and files out of the bar before filing in again, à la Duke of York, a minute or two later; at another, they all let off their guns simultaneously, making a racket that shakes the shaky ceiling. And Barry sings that there's no place he'd rather be than here, with these 'Rednecks, White Socks and Blue Ribbon Beer' . . .

Barry's grin is getting wider as the evening progresses, and his delivery is getting slicker. At the end of a Johnny Cash segue ('A Johnny Cash number?' he says. 'But he doesn't do any of mine . . .') he announces a guest spot, says that Phil is going to sing a couple of numbers, and demands a round of applause. There is a mutter or two amongst the Dixie Gamblers, who have to take their seats again as Phil plays a slightly reggaefied version of 'Sea of Heartbreak'. But they're mollifed when, before his next number, Phil announces that he's Barry's biggest fan; and bugger me if he doesn't sing his own composition, 'Mr Johns', by way of a tribute to the great man, 'who helped me out at a bad time . . .'

Barry stands at the bar, a faux-modest grin on his chops, as Phil delivers. It's a jaunty number, uptempo, in song-and-dance country rhythm, all about a man who always has a smile upon his face:

> *He does Willie Nelson, Merle, George Jones, Waylon and*
> *   Charley Pride*
> *Songs of jealous men and cheating wives*
> *If there's a wedding or a birthday or if your ship sails on*
> *   next tide*
> *There's a song to fit 'most everything in life*

For when he takes the stage the whole place comes alive
And everybody joins in with the fun
The pleasure that he brings with all the country songs he
  sings
Ain't you glad that you're in here with Barry Johns . . .

As tributes go, it's pretty fulsome, especially for someone who's still alive; C&W tributes tend to be elegies, like all those 'Midnight in Montgomery' songs about Hank that the likes of Alan Jackson do. It's Ian who tells the tale, though Phil and Barry both fill bits in later. Phil, it emerges, has been gasping for air in his personal sea of heartbreak, has been struggling to hear a crackling signal of consolation. After going over to pop he developed problems with his hearing. He lost the use of one ear, which was manageable; but along with the strain on the remaining ear came chronic tinnitus that meant he couldn't pick up his guitar without a deep jarring in his brain, and the tinnitus, and the enforced idleness, and being exiled from his music, drove him so close to the edge of madness that he'd tried suicide. He survived, and has now got control of his problem to the point that he can play again, for a limited time only; and Barry, his old mucker, is letting him play a couple of numbers two or three times a week so that he can get back his confidence, so that he can find out how much he can take.

Barry's smile looks a bit different now, and I know I've been unfair to him. I watch him during the last part of his set; he's playing a game, and he knows he's playing a game, as he lets the remaining routines play themselves out. When I die, he sings to finish, I may not go to heaven, but Phil gives him a look like he's an angel already, and he is good. I corner him after he's packed up and ask him if he ever gets fed up with the same pubs, the same songs, the same mother. 'Well, you moan about it,' he says, with a nod to Phil, 'but there are worse lives, aren't there?' And he shows me his guitar. It's an electric, a solid-looking piece, unbranded.

'It was my lifelong ambition to make my own guitar, and now I've done it,' he says; and he says it like it's given him more pleasure than anything else. He lets me have a feel of it, unplugged, and I do a little tinny strum on unamplified steel strings. 'I've to plane it down, like,' he says, watching the fingers of my left hand, 'because the strings are too far from the fret-board, but what do you think of that?' What I think is that when I die I may not go to heaven, but that I'd rather be a Singing 'ammer than an Unsinging one.

Trying to keep our heads above the water ...

As venues go, the Ards Rangers Football Club Social Club is not the most glamorous. Ards Rangers is a little non-league, maybe even an amateur outfit; Ards, their Northern Ireland Premiership neighbours, have a big ground next door – a glittering grandstand with executive boxes (no doubt), a glittering leather-lined social club to match. Ards Rangers Club sits in a pitted car-park of tyre-crunching rocks and pebbles. I get out of the van into the teeth of another wintry wind, and meet a flat hardboard door, scuffed and kicked by thousands of boots, western and football. Inside there's just a long corridor and another flat hardboard door which has a 'Sorry, house full' sign up. A busload has come in from Belfast and swelled the crowd, the woman on the door says. I only just manage to blag my way in.

The Ulster bands, like Barry, patrol their own patch; and though it's a bigger patch, most don't venture mainlandwards and few mainlanders venture this way either; they're not prepared to get on the ferry without a three-gig guarantee, and few British country bands can command the sort of inter-organizer organization that requires. Tracy and the Bar-Room Buddies are an Ulster favourite, and you can see why. They're a sharp, audience-pleasing outfit. They play three-and-three: three slow ones, waltzes and western, for the couples, followed by three uptempo for the line-dancers and the odd disco-head. When they speed up they go rocky in a tight-ship sort of way; when they come downbeat – well, there's *that girl who waits on tables used to wait at home for me*, but there's also some Nanci Griffith, some Lyle Lovett, some Rodney Crowell.

At half-time they come and sit at my table and smoke. Tracy is Silk Cut – a good-looking woman of thirty-odd with a tight black perm cut long and high and a thin, youngish body slipped without strain into a tight black leather skirt and a short, fitted leather jacket. Rod is Regal King Size – tall, with an off-beat rock hairdo, good-looking enough for it to be a shock when he says he was in rock bands as far back as the seventies. That was how he started; his rock band toured England then, and the places he mentions trip off his tongue like blue remembered hills: 'The Batley Variety Club,' he smiles, 'Bingley, Brighouse . . .' But things didn't quite work out and the rest is archetype. He came home, took up country music and became Tracy's Bar-Room Buddy; and it wasn't long until he was her Bedroom Buddy too.

And so life started for them; and now they play, always within fifty miles of Belfast; the key thing, says Rod, is 'to make a wage – to keep our heads above water'. To make the wage – the band takes about £200 a night between the three of them, depending on the size of the venue – they play 200 nights a year – 'and the rest'. They have a three-year-old girl that Rod's parents look after on the evenings they play, which means she's with them four or five nights a week. For now it's fine, because she's not at school; Rod's the getter-up, and even if he's not in bed till three or four he can go and collect her and he and Tracy can spend the day with her before they drop her off again on their way to the next gig; another night, another town, the same childminder. We have a laugh when I ask if she's adopted a rock-and-roll lifestyle – I ask if she's smoking in bed yet – but neither of them looks at ease when I ask what happens when she goes to school; how they can have a relationship with her then is a deep, dark river they've yet to cross. They get up for their next set. *Let's have a round for that young cowboy/ And wish him better luck next time . . .*

I watch them – especially Tracy – all through that third set. As I say, they're very good; but they're hardly stretched up there. Whenever Rod, or the second Buddy, plays a lead, you can see Tracy talking to whoever's idle, her face hard with distraction. She seems to have kept a quiet corner for herself, and the corner's empty even there, even on stage, even in the spotlight. I see them just as we're leaving and go over to wish them good luck. It's Saturday tonight, Rod says; they have another gig on Sunday, then Tuesday, Wednesday, Thursday. A normal week. But every Monday, he says, they keep clear. Not only do they not play any gigs on Monday, they keep their house entirely free of music, a quiet corner for themselves. 'We have rules. I'm not allowed to pick up the guitar,' says Rod. 'She doesn't sing. Not a word. Not even in the bath. We have no LPs on the turntable, no CDs in the player. We don't even have tapes in the car. It's like I say; we're trying to keep our heads above the water.'

Never go to Nashville – they'll break your heart there . . .

Willie Nelson not only keeps his head above the water; he walks on it. Or so the inhabitants of a South American town thought when, after a thunderstorm, what looked like the gaunt, bearded face of Christ began to appear on the blank wall of a shop. Pilgrims, sensing another Lourdes, began to flock to pray at the site; there were reports of cures, of miracles. And when it rained again, the face of another God appeared in the space next to the bearded one; but it was only that of a minor god of love, the Latino smoothie Julio Iglesias. The vision proved to be a white-washed-over poster advertising that awful disco-smooching duet 'To All The Girls I've Loved Before' that the rain had uncovered. And while Willie is a religious man – he was kicked out the Baptists but, via the Aquarian Bible, acquired a belief in reincarnation – he is as made of clay as anyone else when it comes to music, when it comes to dealing with the business part of the music business.

He was certainly not the product of an immaculate conception. His ma and pa, Myrle and Ira, both hopped it and left him in the care of his Texan grandpa, Daddy Nelson, who first taught him to play D, A and G on the guitar, thereby opening the country songbook in its three-chord entirety, and then, by dying when Willie was seven, taught him the bare essentials of how to write heartbreak numbers. Willie went on to write some of the greats of the genre. In 1961 alone he supplied 'Crazy' to Patsy Cline, 'Hello, Walls' to Faron Young and 'Ain't It Funny How Time Slips Away' to Billy Walker. He also, momentously, furnished Ray Price with the original version of the country-blues standard, 'Night Life'. Although it wasn't momentous for him; skint in 1960, he'd sold not only the rights but the writing credit for $150. In the thirty-odd years since, during which it's been covered a hundred times and has sold thirty-odd million copies in one form or another, not only has Nelson's royalty remained stubbornly stuck at $150, but someone else's name is in the brackets after the title.

He expresses no regret for having acted as he did; it taught him that he could write good songs and, in any case, he needed the money having already, at eighteen, a wife and family to support; not just any wife, but Martha, a fiery Cherokee Maid who once tied him up in a bedsheet with skipping-ropes and beat him senseless with a broom-handle. It was, as a friend described it, the 'archetypal fight-and-fuck relationship'; and for several years they fought and fucked their way round the country looking for a stable living. She waitressed in beer-joints or served behind bars; he played in honky-tonks or deejayed on country stations. When, in the year of the building of the Berlin Wall, he had his triple whammy of writing successes, the barely fastened wheels began to come off their union. Playing nights, he began to play away at nights, and soon Country Willie was gone.

When he left Martha for Shirley, Willie seemed to have cracked it. On the strength of his writing credits, he gave up his crazy ways and bought a mansion on the hill with her, and retired to farm the land around it; he stopped playing the juke-joints, put on thirty pounds and began to smoke a pipe. But he longed to make it as a singer as well as as a writer, and he left Shirley behind as he hit the road once more. He married Connie, his third wife, in Las Vegas, without having taken the precaution of dissolving his marriage to Shirley first. The authorities were understanding, as was a new producer, Jerry Wexler at Atlantic, who was prepared to offer him an artistic flexibility that none of the hidebound Nashville producers, worried that his compositions stretched to four and sometimes – gasp! – five chords, could match. He moved back to Texas, to Austin, and made the records, including the spectacularly successful *Outlaw* albums with Waylon Jennings and others, that changed the direction of country music.

By then Willie had learnt the first rule of C&W singing – never trust the record company. In his first contract, he found money was being held back against 'breakages', even though it was years since glass discs had given way to vinyl LPs. He discovered that record company 'expenses' could mean almost anything; that you could open your royalty statement and find that you owed the company money. 'Never go to Nashville – they'll break your heart there,' he told Jennings, when Waylon was just a slip of a lad whose deep, hard voice had just begun to crack. Waylon did, of course, and it did break his heart. An honest country boy, he trusted the suits; once, he put out an album, then went off to promote it for 180 days, then came back to find that he owed the company $31,000. He went to them to borrow some money to pay the band. They came up with the readies, but only when he had agreed to a five-year extended contract on niggardly terms; and, when he set his lawyer on to the company, an audit revealed 180,000 albums unaccounted for. Waylon took a lot of pills, then joined Willie in Austin.

Yet for all he knows about the dirt of the music business, Willie loves the road and the job of being an itinerant singer, a troubadour; if there is one person who renders it grime-free, it's him. He travels to his 150 gigs a year in Honeysuckle Rose, his tour bus; he takes with him his driver, Gator, and his band. 'On the Road Again' has idealistic stuff about it being the life he loves, playing music with his friends, and he talks about playing for love, not for money: 'What I do for a living is to get people to feeling good,' he says. And what if, having played for thirty years, he ended up owing the IRS several million dollars? With the aid of those same friends, he was able to avoid the jailhouse, and he's still playing; and when he goes to Atlantic City, he still turns down the free hotel room in favour of parking Honeysuckle Rose ten miles out of town in a beach-side parking lot and lying in his cot listening to the rain fall on the roof of the bus.

Through the eyes of a cowboy...

In the Waterford Hotel, Grantown-on-Spey, Billy, the compère, is out of his head. (He tells me the next embarrassed day that he rarely takes a drink, that when he does it goes straight to his cerebellum.) Tonight he's trying to frame a complimentary intro for the Steve James Country Band, but he can't quite manage it. *A big hand for Scotland's number two country band*, he says in his soft, teuchter tones when Steve first takes the stage. I see his wife coaching him during Steve's first set, and next time he gets up he tries to make it sound better – *a big hand for Scotland's number two country band, well, when the votes were counted he was number two but he's number one to us* – and only makes it worse. And so it goes on: before the third set *Steve is number two this year but sure to be number one next year*, and, before the encores, *Steve James – voted number two in Scotland to Dez Walters but we're sure he'll be number one next year although we like Dez Walters too and we'll just have to see how everyone votes* . . .

It's a typical night on the road for Steve; typical in the sense that anything can happen. Here in the Highlands, anything does. There are only ten or fifteen people in the room most of the night, and while he puts on a professional show, a little bit of jaundice peeps out in his patter. 'Do yous ever dance here?' he asks, in his best Drumchapel. The dance-floor is as thinly populated as the surrounding mountains. 'Well, do yous want a hoedown?' When the answer is, again, no, he says – 'Aye – well just wait till yous've had a couple more drinks and it's time for the last waltz – then yous'll all want a hoedown.' And it's true; by half-ten or eleven a crowd is in, bopping malcoordinatedly on the floor to 'Ain't Going Down 'Til the Sun Comes Up' and calling for more. 'They come in late because they're farmers and they've been out in the fields till late,' says Billy understandingly, but another local suggests that the beer in the hotel is 'awfy expensive' and those in the know prefer to tank up at home before coming out for a thrash.

Steve gets packed up at about half-past one, two o'clock in the end; the bopping crowds have long gone home. There was a party promised at someone's house, but it doesn't materialize, so there's just the case of lager that Steve has brought. The cans get handed round. John, the drummer, passes; he's the driver. Nick, the guitarist, and Snowy, on bass, drink from the can; Steve has a pint glass, a straight pint glass from a pub, that he takes with him, and he pours his and stands in the cold night air sipping from it. In the absence of the party, the question is, what to do? Is it sleep here, in the lane by the Waterford, then

111

wake at seven so as to get to Elgin in time for the festival's nine o'clock soundcheck? Or is it drive to Elgin now, get there at four, park up by the Town Hall, and wake up there? It's left to John, and as he feels awake, we drive through the night.

It's a bit of a squeeze in their van. As well as the band and the gear, they have extra passengers for the festival weekend. There's Snowy's eight-year-old, who, like a trucker's son, is on the road in the school holidays; and there's Ma Elder, a seventy-five-year-old widow, who's come along to sell the CDs and whom Steve calls Ma Broon after the *Sunday Post* cartoon character. Because of the crush Steve comes with me, with his pint glass and a Game Boy that he plays, obsessively, all the way to Elgin. He gives me a potted history of his career; how he was twenty years in rock, playing Dire Straits and London Boys numbers; how he heard Garth Brooks at the Swinging Doors in Glasgow and it blew his mind and turned him over to country; how now, three years on, he has his country band in the shape that he wants it; how his first wife delivered an unsuccessful 'your music or me' ultimatum; how now, more years on than he cares to mention, he has a new marriage in the shape that he wants it, with both moral and financial support to keep him on the road.

And, he says, he just can't give up the road; it's not just the money, it's the Honeysuckle Rose factor, the experience of touring. In fact, the money is the only thing he thinks of as the disadvantage. Sleeping in the van, in the clapped-out squeeze, is fine; I look at the van as we drive behind it, and everything's rusty except the locks. Being on the road is fine, because there's the company and the craic; sometimes it gets a bit smelly, but at the end of the journey there's always a friend's house, or, at worst, the local swimming-baths, where everyone can have a shower and clean up before the concert. And the concert itself – that remains the great buzz, the moment when it all comes together, the moment that's worthwhile, even if the audience is fifteen pissed-up sheep-shaggers. He looks up from the Game

Boy, as if to suggest that my own life, here on the road, following him, has all these things – except the concert, except the moment that makes it all worthwhile.

'What's the baker's favourite country number?' Steve asks me as we pull in in front of Elgin Town Hall. '"Doughnut Forsake Me O My Darling".' I get out; he doesn't, because he's trapped at some obscure level of the Super Mario. 'D'ye think that's J. C. King's van?' he asks the others of a long white Mercedes van that's alongside. They think it might be but it's not; it's the Mitchells', a brother-and-sister duo from Essex. J C will be here some time tomorrow, as will Dez, Scotland's Number One, as well as the biggest names in British country, Raymond Froggatt and Sarah Jory, who come in fleets of posh vans that are not rusty at all. The band is still wide-awake. It's clear from their eyes that their wakefulness comes from adrenalin and not only because Stuart, Snowy's son, has just been sick in the back. We sit and have another can, then take turns to piss in the municipal bushes before we go to sleep at five.

When I wake, at ten, the band has already sound-checked in; only Ma Elder is in the van, and she's still wide-awake, even though she says that she dropped off at five and woke at quarter-past. I go into the hall for an early sniff around. (It's not an open-air festival, Elgin; when I see a sign saying INDOOR CAR BOOT SALE I realize why.) The early musicians – the Mitchells, a couple of local acts – are hanging round, talking equipment, trading favours, enduring boredom. When I drift back outside Steve is paying the band for Grantown. It's just fifty quid a man; and even then he has to take back a fiver each as a contribution towards the two dozen Tennent's. For Snowy, a tidy forty-year-old from Perth, it's pocket-money, really; he has a recording studio, and this is just indulgence. For the rest it looks a bit closer to the bone, a bit nearer to the stuff of survival, here on level three of the Game Boy of musicianship.

The festival starts, and the Mitchells come on. I'm in the

auditorium with John, Steve's drummer. He's the thinker of the band; Steve is the leader, Nick the spliffing guitarist, Snowy the clean-liver. John has a past; he was a seminarian, but quit the priesthood when someone bought him a drum-kit; and he's a diabetic, so he wanders the towns they stop off in looking for early-morning blood-sugar. He's good (both he and Steve mention that a spectator once described him as 'a drum machine that drinks') and has played in all sorts of diverting-sounding rock and blues bands. ('I have never, ever, ever seen anyone who drank so much or who took so many drugs,' he says of one of his previous band-leaders.) He got interested in country when The The and other grunge bands began fooling around with it. This is his first go at country, and you can see a restlessness in him, a wish to push Steve and his crew on from the Garth Brooks imitation that's Steve's new country trademark.

His analysis is acute; Steve, he says, plays 250 nights a year in C&W clubs. They are classic bread-and-butter gigs; they pay the mortgage, the petrol, the gas-bill. But they also smother, because the C&W club audience – whether they're dancers, or just traditionalists – like only what they like, and they're not generally there to listen to new stuff. 'If you ever hear Steve play one of his own songs,' says John, 'he starts by *apologizing* for it. We should be proud of our own stuff, not end up being defensive about it. But not just that. The stuff we write is all about cowboys. I think we should be writing country songs about what we see here, in this country, in our daily lives. We should go hard on being Scottish; maybe get a fiddler, do some Celtic country. The *Braveheart* thing is big; people are interested. Steve should get out of that Garth Brooks shirt. If we're ever going to go to Nashville, we have to do something different. There's hundreds of bands out there doing this stuff. We have to do something different. And we're Scottish; we've *got* something different.'

Up on stage, the cocky Essex boy and his lovely but trampled-on-looking sister are doing just that; the boy sings one of his own songs about a tramp he saw on the tube, and while John doesn't think much of the song, which is a bit sentimental, he applauds the effort; when they end their set with a rocked-up version – as close to a thrash as C&W people ever go – of 'The Ballad of Davy Crockett', they look like a band that's giving themselves a chance. Steve comes over to give John a five-minute warning. 'Why did the chicken and the drummer cross the road?' he asks. John and I shake our heads. 'The chicken had a gig.' I look in the festival programme, sure I saw something in the notes on Steve, and I was right; it says he is going to Nashville to record in the autumn. So why John's fatalism? 'It's all off,' says John, 'it fell through. But you'd better talk to Steve if you want to know what happened.'

John has to go and set up. I drift out into the lobby and talk to Ann, who runs an Inverness club and books acts both for her own club and as an agent for Scottish and Irish artistes. A man from the Borders interrupts: he's bringing a band up from England in October. Would she like a Monday or a Wednesday if they're with him on the Tuesday? She takes the band, joylessly, explaining to me the crucial economics of splitting expenses between clubs. Though she tells me with a twinkle about her father, who introduced her to 'cowboy' music, she looks over-full of the hard-eyed cynicism of someone who has had too much to do with promoters striving to pay starvation wages, with bands struggling to make it. 'What gets you is the way people behave,' she says, 'all the in-fighting that goes on behind the scenes.' And later, when I ask her who her favourites are she says that 'A good artist is one that pays his commission.'

I hear Steve's band striking up, and, seeking a new angle, climb up to the top of the Town Hall balcony to watch him; I want to give him a chance at stadium rock. He's in good form: 'Do yous like Garth Brooks?' he asks. 'I'll tell him the next time I see him . . .' and he plays a load of Brooks numbers as well as a couple by the Mavericks and a nice number with a line about 'The Big D – And I Don't Mean Dallas . . .' He jumps down from the stage and carries on playing while he sits in the front row next to a middle-aged woman flushed with pleasure, or maybe embarrassment, and he shakes hands with the rest of the front two rows before climbing back up on stage.

All the time he's doing covers he has a whimsical look on his face, as if he's not sure how seriously to take all this stuff; and he does his party-pieces, his impersonations of Willie Nelson and Johnny Cash, his synthesized Glenn Miller medley played through the electric guitar. But when he moves on to the title track of his new CD – when he's apologized for it, just as John said – his eyes take on a different, more searching quality as he scans the crowd. Just as John said, it's not a song about being Scotland's Number Two; it's called 'Through the Eyes of a Cowboy', and, just as John said, you see a different person there; all of a sudden you see someone who, if not obsessed, is ambitious:

> *Through the eyes of a cowboy*
> *To the depths of his soul*
> *His whole way of life*
> *His never-ending goal . . .*

It goes down well. But as the applause rings round, his cowboy eyes fade out and his Drumchapel eyes return: 'You're the best audience we've had all day,' he says. 'Stamp your feet, clap your hands, but don't spill your drink . . .' And, his pub-singer persona restored, he goes back to the Brooks and the Mavericks and the 'I Don't Mean Dallas' numbers.

The band stays on until the evening, for the dance, although it's actually Dez Walters, as Scotland's Number One, who's scheduled to play. Steve has his pint glass with him (the bar is selling cans only, lager and export) and he's wandering around, so I ask him about Nashville; all I know, I tell him, is that he was supposed to go, and he didn't. The tale he tells would make Willie Nelson weep, because even if Willie didn't want Waylon to go to Nashville, there's no doubt that, for such as Steve,

Nashville is the main chance; like young boxers from the projects, there's no point telling them not to get into the ring when what the ring offers is the chance to escape a world of drive-by shootings. Steve wanted – desperately wanted – to go to Nashville, and con-men and tricksters and bullshit-artists let him down.

The story's long, and it comes in two instalments; he has to get up and duet with Dez at one point. In short, a man approached him in Glasgow claiming to be a friend of Garth Brooks and, more feasibly, claiming to represent a promotion company called Nashville Connection. He said he thought Steve had promise, and struck a deal with him: he gave him a wad of money with which to make a CD in exchange for four free gigs; and once the CD was made, and there was something to go on, he would take him to Nashville, where, in exchange, Steve would play four more free gigs. Then, of course, he would be a star, he would be riding in a limousine. And so Steve paid out for the studio, and paid out the balance of having the CDs made; and paid out, too, in the shattering of his dreams when the man disappeared, leaving a half-finished CD and no telephone number. The band rang international directory inquiries and got the number of Nashville Connections; but the only one listed turned out to be a hire company. Of limousines.

There's supposed to be a party tonight, but, again, it doesn't happen; someone's ill, someone's wife's tired, someone forgot to buy the cans. Steve and the band are not too bothered. It's midnight, and they're playing the Millport Festival tomorrow – this – afternoon. And Millport is in south-west Scotland, while Elgin is in north-east Scotland; there's packing up, and then a couple of hundred miles of road, and then a ferry-hop across to the Isle of Cumbrae. And since the ferries will be stowed out from early in the day, the band is going to be in the queue for the 6.45 a.m. one to make sure they get across; that's professionalism, to never miss a gig, to always pay the commission. So with John the Drummer at the wheel, the rest of them settle down to sleep, or suck on cans of Tennent's, in the back. I watch the tail-lights disappear, and, even as I'm glad I'm not, I wish I was going.

I trek back to the camp-site, weary. In the toilet next morning, a man from Huntly, a festival-goer, is shaving. We talk about the hangover his mate is going to have when he wakes up, and then about music, and I tell him that Steve and the boys would have had no more than £100 for their session. 'A hundred pounds for an hour?' the man says. 'That's no' bad.' I describe what the hour entails – an hour's playing, yes, but eight hours' return driving, the sleeping-over, the waiting, the guest duet spot. 'Aye, but an hour – I'd do that job for a hundred an hour.' I ask him if he's staying for the Sunday. 'No,' he says, with the air of someone who knows what hard work is. 'My mate's got a ferm – and he's aye got to get back to pump up the water for the coos.' And he goes off humming a song; it sounds like 'Through the Eyes of a Cowboy'. Or it might have been that other one, that Steve played as a solo spot, at the end. Something about how he could have missed the pain, but he'd have had to miss the dance . . .

'The Big D – And I Don't Mean Dallas'

At Elgin I meet Brigitte, and her man Danny, who's selling badges that say REAL MEN DON'T LINE-DANCE. Brigitte asks what I'm doing and does a bit of light teasing: 'Oh – it's an everyone-has-a-story-to-tell sort of thing?' I say yes. She says, 'I'll tell you my story, if you like.' I switch on my mental notebook, all ears. 'I was born in Germany, I married a squaddie, came to Scotland, it didn't work out, I met Danny. That's the story.' I say thanks, that's very helpful, and we laugh. Next day she completes the saga: 'The divorce was fine,' she says. 'He got the bed, I got the headboard. How about that for amicable?' The answer is pretty good, and it prompts a strong feeling of if-only, a touch of in-my-dreams.

My 'Big D – And I Don't Mean Dallas' – begins in the Yellow Pages. It's a bit of a lottery, getting it all set up. Marital lawyers are not exactly having to tout for business just at the moment, so you're lucky if you can get a cheap half-hour introductory session; and the first lawyer I see, whose name I won't mention since he has a libel specialist partner – well, his idea of a cheap half-hour is sixty quid. He spends quite a lot of the time with his eye on the clock, making sure we don't stray into another-sixty-quid territory, but he's also quite happy to do a Bufton Tufton routine, joshing with his clerk, blabbing on about Oxbridge colleges with remarkable precision, providing half-arsed, patronizing and studiedly vague answers to my inquiries. He doesn't like the look of me, but I don't like the look of him either, so I don't go back; it's a couple of months, and some new crisis, before I can bring myself to arrange to see another one.

I'm careful next time, and, knowing that cheap introductories mean very little, I plump for the one in the book that advertises herself as a mediator as well as a solicitor. And this turns out to be a good move; through the months and months that follow, Julia, notwithstanding the fact that she does not wear a college tie, is endlessly courteous, endlessly reasonable, endlessly prepared to let me try to sort things out on my own and come to her only for ratification, endlessly prepared to go with my irregular flow. And that would be fine, were it not for the fact that Ruby ends up being represented by as matrimonial a lawyer as it's possible for a lawyer to be; someone who seems happy to send off letters about any Tom, Dick or Harry event so long as she can claim her hundred pounds at the end of the day.

Well, that may be unfair – she is only following orders – and later on in the process I know that she talks hard and sensibly to Ruby; but at the start I have to read documents discussing in detail whether my mother – ostracized after, in a stressed moment, she asked the Greek how she was to know that he wasn't a child-molester – should be allowed access to the children; and I receive a load of other papers that deal, as the

119

cash-register rings, with things that could have been settled in a two-minute phone-call between Ruby and me. Suspicious of me (and wealthier than me), Ruby seems to make an appointment with her lawyer whenever she has a problem, and she talks it over, and pays her sixty quid, and the lawyer, for another sixty quid, writes to my lawyer, who for sixty quid reads the letter and sends it to me, and I tear it up or ring Ruby to tell her either that, of course, it's obvious that what she says is true, or that she's barking and no one in their right mind could accept what she says as a basis for action.

And so it drifts on aimlessly for months; petitions and minutes get written, of course, but everything else, unless you want to go nuclear on your solicitor's bills, has to be talked out between you. And the stupid thing is that in the end what has to be sorted out comes down to only three or four things. There's house, and there's money, and there's things, and there's children; and they may be a big three or four things, but that's all there are, and people who were in a rational state or meeting to agree a bit of business would be able to work something nice and compromise-y out in, say, three or four one-hour sessions. But in the absence of mediation (Ruby refuses to go to a mediator, believing it will just turn out to be a talking-shop for my benefit) the three or four things must be dealt with in emotional, painful snatches.

And without mediation, there's no one to make you understand the crucial fact of the negotiations that follow the end of a marriage; that you can't get anything from a marriage break-up without taking it directly from the other person; and since the other person is likely, by now, to be someone you detest, that process of giving-and-taking is highly unlikely to benefit from anything resembling give-and-take. So instead of giving and taking, you've trouble and strife, you've plague and pestilence, you've bickering that would embarrass Tweedledum and Tweedledee.

All you can do is to try to hold on to those three or four

important things; so where do we stand? Pretty square on some. Practically, if not emotionally, Ruby accepts my claim to primary care of our children; she goes out to work, I work at home. We've already divided our things; give or take the odd spat, more about symbolism than reality, we are straight on that front. We have some sort of agreement about money, and even if she has halved the original maintenance figure, the original figure was unsustainable, and I don't really want her money anyway. All we're left with is house; the territory of the house, perhaps, but more likely the selling of it and the working out a percentage for division of the spoils. I'm sure that to many divorcers this will seem simple, child's play, just a financial equation, nothing in comparison with the dirt that gets dished when the children are being fought over; but the stuff sits on my and her and the lawyers' tables, unattended to except in a desultory way, waiting for the next crisis or the next agreement to push *Jarndyce versus Jarndyce* on another glacial inch.

The bends are always on the corners ...

My singing career moves on just as slowly. I never get to sing, either with Barry or Steve or Tracy or Willie. (I get to talk a whole lot, but it's not the same.) Until my guard drops for a minute, and I'm not expecting it, and I get dragged on stage against my will.

I've had enough of cowboys and pardners and am in the mood for a break. I've been camping in a toiletless and showerless car-park of a Cornish Wild West village; I'm feeling permanently dirty and temporarily sated with the melancholy whine of the steel guitar, so I pull into the first camp-site I find, resolving to spend the evening, such as it is up to the time I take an extremely early night, washing and writing and smoking and drinking whisky. I pick a roadside camp-site at random, looking for nothing but anonymity, a quiet corner for myself.

At first I have no suspicion that I have fallen into a trap. Sure, I can see that the place is newly made, that it's more building-site than camp-site; and though there's no one else camping there it seems like it has the advantage of solitude after several days of being completely unalone. The owner, Bernard, is sitting on a chair with black gardening hands; he's been working on the place. He has been landscaping the site in a brutalist sort of a way; pouring concrete in to make a pond, setting old Skoda chairs in concrete to make a rest area under a patio roof. I drift over and pay him the £1.50 he asks for (the going rate elsewhere is £7–8). I'm so sure I've escaped that when he asks me what I'm doing in his part of the world I tell him, and a grin splits his face so wide it looks like it will fall apart at the seams. He lifts up his grubby gardening top and there, on the grubby gardening jeans, is a huge belt-buckle with a silver dollar pressed into a niche in the centre. 'Country and Western, eh? Well, I'm your man . . .'

The belt is a gift from some country singer that I've never heard of, but Bernard has had a career of his own in Country and Western. He has played bass with a man called Jess Owen, a reasonably distinguished British C&W singer in the sixties. (In true C&W style Owen was a father of the absentee variety; Bernard pulls out a clipping from the *Sun* in which his son, the actor Clive, talks about his feeling for his long-gone daddy.) Jess Owen, Bernard tells me, packed it all in in the seventies and became a school janitor. Now he's back on the road, playing again; he's put together a 'combo' (it's Bernard's favourite word, that, the mark of the professional) called Jess Owen and the Caretakers.

'Caretakers': Bernard pronounces the word with extreme Yorkshire relish. Not that I've had to do much to assess the origins of Bernard's accent. He tells me repeatedly that he's from Batley, and he interrogates me about my Yorkshire connections. 'Married, Ste-ephen?' I say that I was, that she was from Harrogate. 'Eeeeh,' says Bernard, 'you like your Yorkshire puddings, then—' In deference to all the girls I've loved before, I visualize this in culinary, rather than sexual, terms. His obsession with establishing his origins and making a connection between us is not so much to establish that he comes from Yorkshire as to make it clear he does not come from Cornwall. He's obsessed with the stupidity of those who live around him, putting it down to in-breeding; Cornwall is the Kentucky backwoods as far as Bernard is concerned, and if he steps out the door he's as likely as not to end up on all fours getting shagged by a porky hillbilly, like Burt Reynolds's friend in *Deliverance*.

'Your Cornishman, Stee-phen – it's mebbe stopped now, but you go back to t'eighteenth century, and what d'you find? Your Cornishman's sitting around in his slate cottage wi' nowt to do. "What shall I do?" he says to himself. "Eeeeh-up – I'll go and get me leg over with me sister."' He isn't smiling, though it's a trick of his to lead you along before exploding into firecracker laughter. 'In-bred, you see. Can never get a lick o' sense out of them. They're all Bennies.' And he explains that troops in the Falklands called the Falklanders Bennies, imagining them genetically disadvantaged; 'Bennies. Like Benny from *Crossroads*.' He mimes a slack-faced mongol look and laughs uproariously. 'The thing is, when the officers find out, they decide they have to do summat about it, right? So they ban the squaddies from calling the local people Bennies. And what happens? Next day the squaddies are calling them Stills. Stills, Stee-phen. Because they're Still Bennies.'

He takes me inside for a cup of tea, which soon turns into a Bacardi and Coke, and we take a run through his photo albums and scrapbooks. He has a publicity shot of Jess Owen, and he points out Screaming Lord Sutch, for whom he once played bass. Now, he is where all country singers go when they die; he plays cabaret in Holland for a portion of the year before retiring to Cornwall for the summer. He is hoping to get the camp-site going as a regular summer earner and tells me he's interested in having a country festival there – 'Y'know, put up a mar-quee, a drinks tent, have a day's music . . .' But for the moment, that most western of notions, a land dispute, is dogging his life.

'My father taught me one thing,' says Bernard. 'He took me to a high wall and said, "Jump – I'll catch you." So I jumped – and he moved out the way. Aye – I fell. And he picked me up after bit and said, "Son – never trust anyone, not even your own father."' Bernard's own distrust sent him down to St Austell or Truro to have a look at the Ordnance Survey map (a brilliant malapropist, he calls it the Audience Survey) and then to the county planners, where he discovered that one of his neighbours had assumed a bit of his smallholding, a little corner of land across the road. The other bloke had been tilling it nine years, and in three more would have been able to claim it under the law of Adverse Possession, which Bernard calls Advised Possession. Bernard is preparing a campaign, using lawyers; not local ones, of course, not hillbillies, but family ones, even though the lawyer in the family is a recently bereaved alcoholic currently living in Australia.

We go to the pub together; I drive, at his insistence, and I don't drink any more, at his insistence, and after he's spent my £1.50 on his first pint he bums the price of another couple off me before we set off home. On the way there and on the way back he has a line in surrealistic chat. 'What y'have to remember, Stee-phen, is that in Cornwall, the bends are always on the corners.' In the pub he starts pursuing the barman, a Brummie who's a friend of Raymond Froggatt, about his plans for a festival; would the barman set up and run a bar for it? He's thinking of a one-day event, but as he talks about it it occurs to him that it might be two, with everybody sleeping over in his camp-site and the police paid off. 'Well, they're all masons, they know how to turn a blind eye . . .'

On the way back he looks in the back of the van and he sees the guitar there. Say no more; he insists that I bring it inside and that we have a session. It's about midnight now, and when his wife comes home from the late shift at the old folks' home,

Bernard, who I've come to think of as Benny, is well on the way and slurring slightly. He pulls his huge bass amp out the cupboard and he sets up his reverb microphone on a big metal stand; before long I've given him 'Swinging Doors' and 'Folsom Prison Blues' and he's played me some Willie Nelson numbers. Then the bug begins to bite him. 'I've got this idea,' he says, 'for a weekend festival. My son's got a rockabilly band, you know. Did I play you his record? Well, he'd come. My brother John would come down. He can play folk, rock, country, anything. Have I played you his tape? And you and I – we could do a double-header, you and I. You've a nice voice. And a nice picking action . . .'

Soon we begin to lose the country feel, and he pulls out his songbooks and starts giving me the full cabaret works into the microphone, there in his inglenook living-room; he even starts telling jokes. ('Hear about the Irish bobsleigh team? Got stuck on the way up. Two Chinese people got divorced. She went back to Peking. He went back to Wanking.') And the more drunk he gets, the more he thinks I need a musical lesson. 'Take the lead from bass and drums,' he says, as he drags me through a relentless series of cabaret pop-songs – 'The Air That I Breathe', 'Mystery Train' – while I strum along. I go to bed at two with my head ringing with the effort to keep him on George Jones and Willie Nelson while he tours the Dutch cabaret circuit of his mind.

In the morning, up for a pee, I hear Benny blabbing to his wife in the kitchen and I assume they are arguing; but they are laughing hysterically, perhaps at me. Still, I've had my chance to sing, albeit before a more selective audience than I had in mind when I started. Later, ready, I am going to knock on the kitchen door and say goodbye, but there is no one in. So I simply leave, my triumph fading as I drive. Another town, another day, I think. But about three weeks later the phone rings and a broad, grating voice says: 'Who do you think this is?' To his great delight, I get Benny first time. We chat for a bit – he asks me if

125

my maintenance payments have been set by the 'CSI' – and I say I'll see him again, maybe. 'I've been having this idea,' he says, 'for a three-day festival . . .'

CHAPTER FIVE

Eighteen Wheels and a Dozen Roses

The longer the road holds you, the more songs you know . . .

'A lot of truckers play Country and Western,' says George. He used to be one, though he's a Tillingbourne bus-driver now, ferrying schoolchildren around Sussex and Surrey. 'I would say a good seventy-five, eighty per cent. You stop any trucker at a traffic light and say, "What are you playing?" and you'll find that they've got a country or a western tape on, be it old stuff or new stuff. When I used to do continental lorry-driving and I'd get to Zeebrugge' – he calls it 'Zee-broodge' – 'I'd have been abroad for seven, eight days and I'd be sick of listening to the same half-a-dozen tapes – so the other drivers would say, "What've you got?" I'd say, "I've got Alan Jackson." "Oh, haven't heard him for a while –" And you end up swapping around. Then you stop at Zee-broodge next time and you say, "What've you got?" and they say, "What about Alan Jackson?" and you say, "That was my old tape anyway," and it's got your name scratched inside it like . . .'

George likes all sorts of C&W styles; as a westerner he likes Frankie Laine and Marty Robbins and Johnnie Horton and the ballads of the old west that Johnny Cash used to do. But he also likes trucking songs. 'What is it that the trucker likes about C&W? It's the good, steady, easy beat. As you're driving along and the diesel engine's going thump, thump, thump, the music needs to go right along with it. You put some country on, and after a while you stop hearing the engine; you hear a thump, thump, thump, but it's the thump, thump, thump of the beat, not of the engine, you're hearing. Nice and steady. And the words – nine times out of ten you're on your own on the road and you sit there singing to yourself. And the further you go, the longer the road holds you, the more songs you know. It's as simple as that, really.'

Any listing of famous battlefields should include my marriage . . .

It's just another reason for philistines to laugh at C&W: trucking. All that bastardized CB-talk about big rigs and Smokey Bears and getting us a convoy. One school of thought says that truckers have good C&W antecedents, for what are truckers but the pioneers of today? What are they but black-top cowboys, new frontiersmen, driven to drive wherever the road takes them? But the metaphor breaks down in the end; the original frontiersmen didn't have Shell account cards, didn't stop for fry-ups at Granada truck-stops. Of course there's something romantic about the idea of driving along a Montana freeway, that image of six days on the road ending with the homeward run, the *I'm on the run, the highway is my home* thing, but that's more to do with flight than with being home, home on the range.

In fact I like trucking music, to a point; I even like the so-bad-it's-good-stuff, and possess a copy of *Teddy Bear*, an album of Red Sovine's three-hanky talkover weepies. But if I'm driving I rarely reach for trucking music specifically; because even if the road is a wilderness that has to be blazed through, well, any country music will do you for that road, any good C&W-er will help you make it through the night. C&W is perfect driving music because it's music to be alone to, music about being alone. If I'm on the road I'll reach for almost any lonesome sounds; but for preference, someone male, someone low and plain and deep, a Johnny Cash or a Merle Haggard.

If both those voices speak of life, of experience, then, in Merle's particularly, there's a low, plain hum that speaks of it feelingly. 'Like a razor's edge, Merle Haggard sings,' was John Stewart's description of that voice, and Haggard's early life was lived on the edge of a razor. A child of *Grapes of Wrath*-style Okies from (near) Muskogee, his family dusted the Dustbowl off their feet in the 1930s. Their destination was California, the Golden State, the land of milk and honey; but not having the do-re-mi, they ended up living in a converted box-car, as hillbillies always do in these archetypal hardship tales. Merle's childhood was tough ('Mama's Hungry Eyes', 'They're Tearing the Labour-Camps Down') and his youth little better; his father died when he was nine, and, no matter how much 'Mama Tried', Merle became a bad boy. Emerging from Reform School – an 'Institute of Lower Education', he calls it – at age seventeen he married a waitress and had four quick children with her. It was not a happy marriage. 'Any listing of famous battlefields,' he said later, 'should include my marriage to Leona Hobbs.'

His four children he supported by a variety of means, but especially by armed robbery. (He's not C&W's only convict by any stretch: Cash too went to jail for a bit; my old mucker Johnny Paycheck got nine-and-a-half years for aggravated assault; and David Allan Coe, who wrote Paycheck's 'Take This Job and Shove It', is said to have killed another prisoner while a non-paying guest of the State of California.) Merle first spent ninety days in the slammer and then, on his release, tried to rob a restaurant while too drunk to have the sense to check that the owner had gone home; two-and-a-half years. Inside, one of the great meetings of music history occurred; Haggard was a con in the audience on one of the nights that Cash played for the prisoners of San Quentin. Hearing songs about a life as hard as his own, Merle joined the prison band, resolving to make something out of his misfortunes.

And so he did: the labour-camp songs were followed by a chain of memorable prison numbers which so catch the strain of loneliness that they're perfect for long stretches of solitary highway; there's 'Branded Man' and 'Sing Me Back Home' for starters, and then the sublime 'I'm a Lonesome Fugitive'. (They're songs that I thought all prisoners would feel for; though when I searched for C&W prisoners, the man from the Prison Reform Trust told me that nine out of ten prisoners prefer heavy metal.) Released, Merle went to live in Bakersfield, where he and Buck Owens inspired a breed of younger musicians to take to the Bakersfield Sound which, as Nashville went cloying and over-instrumentalized, managed to stay plain and spare and rootsy. With his lean, tough singing backed by his lean, tough band playing songs of his lean, tough life, he began to edge his way forward; by the nineties he had more than forty country Number Ones, and only St Conway de Twitty has more than that.

So far, so good. But any Merle-listening session runs into problems. You've heard 'Silver Wings' and '(If You're Trying to Break My Heart) You Don't Have Very Far to Go' and 'Kern River', maybe even my daughter's favourite, the ever-so-slightly wistful-to-the-point-of-cloying 'Daddy Frank (The Guitar Man)'; and you know about his sympathy with blue-collardom, and you know about his tribute-work, the way he recorded Jimmie Rodgers and Bob Wills songs as a mark of historical respect. But then along comes 'Okie From Muskogee', the redneck, anti-hippie anthem, which he may or may not have written as a joke; but even if he did, did he write 'The Fightin' Side of Me' (précis: don't speak anti-Vietnam to me or I'll kick your head in) as a joke? Before too long he was hanging around with Richard Milhouse Nixon and (Nixon was a shrewd manipulator of the C&W constituency) bringing in the votes.

And that's why C&W needs the likes of Johnny Cash: 'A lot of people think of country singers as right-wing, redneck bigots; I don't think I'm like that,' he says. He has the credentials; that gutturally, almost sepulchrally rumbling bass voice speaks in just the same way of life lived, yet from Johnny's lips comes nothing but political sense. His sixties and seventies concept albums had right-on themes – the working man and the American Indian, as well as the old west; and he has a death threat from the KKK to testify to the effectiveness of his maligned Indian narrative, 'The Ballad of Ira Hayes'. Meanwhile, he claims to always wear black – he is, remember, the Man in Black – as a comment and a reminder of all the injustice in the world; though another school of thought says that he just doesn't like rhinestones.

Cash's prison recordings and concerts – like the one Merle heard – speak of the same kind of commitment. *Johnny Cash at Folsom Prison* is a heavy contender for best country album of all time, and the sleeve-notes are Cash's dark meditations, as rumbling as his refrains, on prison life. He writes about counting the bars on the window, about the measurement of wealth and power by tobacco, about envying the cockroach that scuttles under the door, and about how doing these things makes a man rot. And he asks listeners to the album, recorded live in the prison, to listen carefully to the precise resonances of the noises off; to the clanging of doors and the whistling of men; but, most of all, 'the single pulsation of two thousand heartbeats in men who have had their hearts torn out' by being deprived of 'all the things that make a man'. The prisoners, he says, are 'all brothers of mine', fellow-participants in the 'Folsom Prison Blues'.

Cash himself has only spent three days in jail; this brotherhood is not Merle's, isn't Allan Coe's. (He was there, he jokes on *Johnny Cash at San Quentin*, for picking flowers.) So if he speaks of loneliness and pain, he is pricked by sympathy, by fellow-feeling. His razor's-edge came not in childhood, though he was born poor, to Arkansas cotton-pickers selected to reclaim marshland on the banks of the Mississippi; 'How High's the Water, Momma?' tells you all you need to know about how that agricultural experiment ended. No; Cash's razor's-edge came after he'd left the army, when his boom-chicka-boom rhythm, the perfect foil for his hard, deep vocal musing, had propelled him on to a 300-gig-a-year schedule that had him popping pills to get out of bed in the morning and drove him pretty close to crazy. (When he left the Opry, in the early sixties, he reportedly smashed all fifty-two stage-lights on his way out of the theatre.) Eventually he found God, wrote a biography of St Paul called *The Man in White* and, converted, cleaned up. But his godsquad-hood is unevangelical and unrighteous and full of sympathy for those still falling; when he sings 'Were You There When They Crucified My Lord?' you sense that he's aware of the sort of daily crucifixions that have little to do with Calvary.

That's why he's Brother Cash, because he's proof that you don't have to be a Republican to love your country; that you can sing lonesome songs without a streak of southern bigotry in you. He's had some silly seasons, like all who've spanned the decades like he has, but to hear an album like the recent *American Recordings* is to understand how much bad taste is producer-led; give him a good man behind the console and Johnny's voice will ring true. There ain't hardly a truck in the driveway of Johnny Cash's *œuvre*; but it is trucking, it is driving music. It's trucking music because – and the road is life, of course – his road, as he says, has seen some 'hard travelling'.

This time I'm going to bake the wedding-cake myself . . .

I'm due to meet John at Swansea services at eight o'clock on a Tuesday morning. I have planned to drive through Monday and sleep in the car-park; but pre-menstrual madness breaks out and Ruby, who spends her weeks away from the children bewailing their absence, is passing the time she has with them by losing the rag with me. She adjudges that I have been ringing too much (twice in a fortnight, plus a couple of calls deliberately left unreturned), so she has the Greek announce that I will no longer be allowed to talk to the children on the phone. The solicitor clarifies that this is out of order, so Ruby decides that, when the holiday is up, she is going to keep one of them. Not both, just one; meaning one wrenched out of orbit and the other, left behind, wondering not only why the other was taken, but why he was left.

The solicitor clarifies that it's unlikely, after all this time, that even Screaming Lord Sutch's nominee for Lord Chancellor would separate the children. But by the time I've talked to everyone who should know, it's eleven o'clock at night. I have no option; I pack up and set off at half-past twelve. It feels like a long, weary journey when I look at the map (A165, M62, M18, M1, M42, M5, M50, A40, M4), but I line up a string of tapes and get some trucking tracks on, one for each stretch of the road, and soon the route is marked by songs, not numbers. There's 'Caffeine, Nicotine, Benzedrine (And Wish Me Luck)', 'Diesel Cowboy', 'Ten Miles From Home', 'Six Days on the Road'. And as the night gets to its darkest point, you begin to feel affection for the passing lorries, the big rigs, whose fairy-lights and flashed signals break the monotony of the white-edged black; and, alone there, you find it impossible not to wonder about the lives inside the cabs, the way that money or love or the absence of either forces the pace of the drivers' lives in the way no speed-limiter could do.

Faron Young is singing 'Almost Dawn in Denver' as the sun comes up; for me, in the Welsh hills, beautiful, with morning flocks stirring dewily, it's 'Almost Dawn in Aber'. As the sun comes up and the lights on the trucks begin to get switched off, the truckers' lives I've wondered about become less romantic; the drivers start to emerge from their sleeping-bags, and I see one, in a string vest, pissing down the side of his gleaming, truck-stopped wagon. I still feel part of a fraternity, though; when I get to the services at half-past six and, bleary, put my head down for an hour, I get up and piss too, eat a horrible bacon roll and, feeling sick as a dog, get myself over to the roundabout to wait for my ride.

John's an ordinary sort of bloke and his bottle-green truck's an ordinary sort of Volvo; when we set off we drive at an absolutely unvarying speed-limited fifty-five, a steady-state twenty-miles-per-gallon trundle, back along the M4 towards the Severn Bridge. We're bound for Devon, which is where John lives, though he's Welsh originally. The truck belongs to a steels stockholder in Llanelli, and today – as every day – it's carrying a mish-mash delivery of bits of metal, of girders, sheets and spars; some lie flat on the flat-bed, and some are stashed so that, over our heads, they lean perilously on the cab roof. Since we're passing the Port Talbot steelworks, I ask if that's where the stuff comes from. Silly of me. 'It's Swedish, Japanese, Romanian, even Croatian,' John says. 'It's all shit stuff. But that's what people want, in this day and age. And now it's so depressed around here, so depressed back in Llanelli, with nothing doing, nothing going on . . .'

He sees another company lorry making its way back there, and he reaches for the CB and checks out the road conditions on the other side of the Severn. I ask about the CB; it's used less for chatting, he says, less for loneliness, less in the C. W. 'We Got Us a Convoy' McCall way as for passing messages about traffic conditions, about police roadblocks, about Ministry checks. 'Oh, and about naked women,' says John. 'If a naked woman's passing, then that thing's buzzing.' He smiles; his small face has craggy features. 'At one time all the company lorries coming back from Wiltshire and Devon would meet at Cardiff services, and then, at Swansea, we'd meet up with the lorries coming back from the Valleys, and we'd make a big convoy home. One day this girl was driving along in a car, a convertible; and she had her dress all undone, blowing in the wind, and nothing underneath. And she passed the convoy, driving – sort of *lingering* – alongside each truck in turn for about a minute;

and from the way she was smiling you would swear she was having an orgasm with each one. That smile! I tell you, you just never know what's round the next corner . . .'

His voice, liltily Welsh, warms to the theme. 'Yes – you see everything from up here in the cab, you know. You might see a woman breast-feeding; or see down into another woman's blouse. The other day two little girls in a school-bus flashed at me – just little pips they had, you know. There was this other one,' he says, 'this woman, and she's giving her bloke, who was driving, a hand-job – as he's driving along! And this mate of mine, in the convoy, he waves to her. And she waves back. She didn't stop doing it . . . she just used her other hand, you know? It's a funny old world, you know. A sick world, actually. Yes,' he ends precisely, 'you never know what's round the next corner.'

I look round the cab, half-expecting porno pics to festoon the bunk area. And while there is a copy of *Escort* lying there, along with a crossword magazine and his *Southern Country* listings, his in-cab gallery is mainly made up of pictures of the Haley Sisters, a pair of sweet, innocent and fully clothed country singers from Bradford. I have a glance in his tape-box, and it's full of stuff by women singers with the same pure sound; he likes Sarah Jory and Amanda Norman Sell and Crystal Gayle and the Judds. Four or five of his twenty tapes are Haleys ones. He used to follow the Haleys around, when he was driving less repetitive routes; he would find out where they were playing and park up for the night there, see them in a club, go to sleep and set off again next morning.

He used to like American country; he used to like trucking numbers, and we chat about a few; but in the end he says that he got bored with them because 'All the songs just tell the same old story.' He agrees when I suggest that maybe that's because his run – with twenty drops on an average trip – has no lone and level stretches, no Big Sky; and trucking music, as George the bus-driver would say, is for that kind of place, for those times when the diesel whine sets your mind into a rhythm and you need to break it with a rhythm of your own. John's run is more or less regular; three trips a week up from his home in Devon, empty; three trips back from Llanelli, with a load of deliveries to small businesses in the West Country.

This afternoon we do about half of them, criss-crossing Devon, popping into Somerset; Bude is kept for tomorrow for the circuitous homeward route. The businesses have a remarkable variety, and every time we stop at a new and unusual one, John chants his mantra about not knowing what's around the next corner. And it is amazing, the variety of ways people make a living. There are orthodox builders and engineers and fabricators and agricultural machinists, but we also deliver to a Formula 2 racing-car team, to a gunsmith, to a miniature steam railway, to a potato-grower turned maker of potato-growing tools, to a man who converts lorries into double yellow line-painters. John tells me about some other regular stops: a sculptor who made an iron woodpecker to knock on the wooden gate of a big house near Hyde Park, a blacksmith who worked a fence for an enclosure at Edinburgh Zoo.

Little bits of trucking folklore are passed on as we drive. He tells me about the gay truckers; about an ex-navy trucker whose CB handle is Gaylord, about another who has a condom on his aerial, about another – a cowboy-hatted, tight-jeaned camp-king code-named Blue Vein – who has pink frilly curtains in his cab and a pink frilly duvet on his cab bunk. 'Don't ask me how I've seen the inside,' says John, 'but I have.' We nearly get run off the road by a tipper, and he tells me about the brotherhood of drivers, how they'll all trust each other, blindly respect each other's light-flashes on the motorway; but tippers? 'Tippers are a law unto themselves.' He tells me about the people you see, time after time, as you pass through small towns; the octogenarian woman with the purple hair, the man standing at his door, always in the same place. And we drop and we stop and we stop and we drop until more than half the load is gone and John, almost home, begins to relax; he drops me at a B&B in Braunton where I sleep for twelve hours and still make our early-morning rendezvous.

Next day I'm sharper, more on the ball; he's cleaner, having been home; he has a clean shirt, clean trousers, a new bag of snap. He's thoughtful, too, for some reason, and starts talking about accidents, as if a question of life and death has just struck him. He tells me about his only head-to-head, how a woman in a car with a child skidded underneath his wheels; when he ran out to see if they were all right, they were, and the baby, in the back, was saying over and over, 'Bad driving, Mummy.' 'Now that's what I call an intelligent baby,' he says.

He tells me about his brush with death; not in a head-to-head crash, but in a himself-against-the-weather clash; how at one time, working for Argos, he'd been making his way from Castleford across the M62 when the snow started coming down, and he'd been the last lorry on to the hill before the road was closed. The wind was blowing wild; as they crossed a viaduct, the van in front turned over, and John was left sitting in his cab as the snow began to pile up one side, covering the window. He managed to get out, but was wearing only a T-shirt and the temperature was way below zero. He heard a Pilkington Glass driver opposite call out, 'Hey Taff!' and he made for him, but every time he stood up the wind blew him down, and by the time he'd crossed the central reservation his hands had gone blue.

He reckons he only just made it, and wouldn't have had Pilkington not had a flask of hot soup which brought his colour back. Mountain rescue got the two of them out of the cab ('Amazing fellows, those blokes') and over to Granada services, where, with two or three hundred others, he and Pilkington were stranded for two days. (The stay has left him forever anti-Granada: 'They wouldn't even give us a free cup of coffee. For two days!') And when he went back for the lorry only the gale-battered cab was left; the entire structure of the trailer had been blown away, the walls, the frame, everything – wrecked by the wind and the weather. 'There but for the grace of God,' he says. 'You never know what's round the next corner.'

He goes quiet and I watch him for a bit. Even on the open road, away from the responsibility of deliveries, he's a fiddler. I watch him drink a drink, eat a Fruit Corner yoghurt, check his schedule, check the map, check the C&W listings, turn around to find something in his bag; all with one hand on the wheel and another lorry up ahead. 'Drivers – real drivers – can do anything as they drive along. You only really need one hand,' he says. He sees an Eddie Stobart truck, one of those ubiquitous green ones with the smart-woollied drivers, the ones with the fan club game you can buy in the service stations; and he tells me that, amongst the fraternity of the road, Eddie Stobart has a bad name; Stobart's phenomenal success has, it seems, driven smaller firms out of business. 'If I see a trucker stuck, under a nine-foot-three bridge, say, I'd always help him out, give him a tow. But not a Stobart. And that's how most of us feel.'

We cross the Severn again. ('You don't have to pay to get out of Wales,' he says, 'but you have to pay to get back in; you can imagine the ribbing I take on the CB about that.') As we begin the backward trip along the M4 he asks if I mind if he drops by Cardiff Airport; he needs to check out where the long-stay car-park is, because he's due to go on holiday soon. Of course I don't, though in the end we get lost and the detour takes about an hour. But in that time it emerges that this is no ordinary holiday; it's a honeymoon. In his – I imagine – late forties or early fifties, John is tying the knot with a woman named Lynn whom he has met in Devon and who, he says, has transformed his life.

And contrary to the image created by the porno mags and the cab-window leering, he tells me how he behaves with her; how they do nice things, like going twitching: 'It brings you together, sort of thing, doing nice things like that.' How they've been to the Isle of Lundy, and how they just walk: 'Well, it's not the sex at our time of life,' he says. 'It's the company more than anything.

Not that I'm saying we don't get up to a bit of fun; she's no prude, is Lynn, and we can have a giggle; she'll even have a look at the old *Escort* now and again. But I wouldn't dream of two-timing her; and it's nice to be able to say that and be so sure about it, after all that happened to me last time.'

I'm curious about last time, and when I ask it brings on a flurry of head-shaking. He tells me that he should never have married his first wife; he was in the Merchant Navy and seeing an Australian woman and he should have gone back for her, like Ernest Tubb in *Filipino Baby*, but met his wife and stayed put. 'Biggest mistake I ever made,' he said. 'I had the passage booked and everything, and the week before I was going on the *Canberra*, I went into a pub in Llanelli; and I met the wife and I came home changed.' He pauses for a moment, fiddles with his sun-shade or his specs or his tape-deck. 'So I wrote a "Dear John" letter to the one in Australia. I tell you, I regretted doing that for twenty years until two years ago, when I met Lynn; only two years ago did I get glad that I didn't go.

'I'm not saying it was always bad with my wife; we got on all right for a while, and I always say she's been a good mother to the children. But we never really got it together after Donna was born; she went kind of frigid, you know, and we never quite put it right. At that time I was working in the steelworks, but I got made redundant, and I was four years on the dole until I got the HGV licence and took a job driving out of Llanelli. But after a while I stopped wanting to go home, there was so much friction, so many arguments. So I made an arrangement with some other drivers; I would drive to London with the loads, and another driver would bring a truck down to the Severn Bridge; and we'd swap over, and I'd go back to London; I would just never go home in the week.

'Stupid, isn't it? What a fool I was. I'd only spend the one day at home, the Saturday; and even then I'd go and watch my son play rugby rather than stay in with my wife. And through the week I lived in the cab. I'd drive to London and park up for the night, somewhere out near the M25, it could be anywhere. And I'd get on a tube and travel round and round for an hour – exactly an hour – reading the *Evening Standard*. And wherever I was at the end of an hour, I'd get off, and I'd go into a pub there and get out of my head with the drink, and then I'd get the tube back and watch TV and listen to music and sleep it off in the cab. And the same the next day, and the next day, and the next. Always the same; until I broke away, got out of all that, until I moved down to North Devon.'

The tale over, he switches the volume up again on the stereo. As he plays the Haleys now, and some other things from his box of sweetness – 'I Want to Be a Cowboy's Sweetheart', 'Blue Skies Over Georgia', a countrified version of 'I Will Always Love You' – it's hard to get away from the image of him filling his cab with sweet sounds when the world all around him smelled of shit; I imagine him coming back to the cab, too drunk for his *Escort*, and lying back and letting this stuff fill his air. He, in his reluctant way, is modest: 'It could have been some other band, I don't know. It just happened to be them.' But when he talks about them, these pretty girls plastered all over his cab, and how he knows them and they know him and they treat him like an uncle and come and sit on his knee when he sees them in a club; well, it's hard to avoid the idea that their sound didn't constitute a dream of love when everything else in his life had fallen to pieces.

And now the dream of love – of a new, mature love – has come true, one way or another, and Lynn has a little spot on his pull-down sun-shade; four or five photos of a woman in reactolites who's too far away for me to have a good look at. 'I was a baker, in the navy, you know; and this time I'm going to bake the wedding-cake myself. For some reason I want to marry her,' he says, 'I don't just want to live with her. I can't really say why. It's not that I'm jealous, or possessive. I think it's something to do with putting things right. Lynn and I don't really argue; it's like I know now, that if you do certain things – if you even *say* certain things, there's no going back on them. You can say something in a temper, but you have to know that you're taking a risk, that you might be about to spoil something, and that the something you spoil might never come back – you know what I mean? But it's only by personal experience that you learn it; that you learn to be *careful* . . .'

He drops me off back at the place where we started. We rummage around in the tape-bin in the shop and he goes off to begin again; to load up at Llanelli, to sleep in the cab – in a different frame of mind now – to begin the journey back to the place he loves and the woman he has learned to love; or the woman who is the beneficiary of his having learned how to love. I drop in at the Pines in Swansea, and watch a bit of B. J. Curtis's act, keeping myself to myself; I don't stay all night. I want to get back home myself, back along all those roads in reverse order, back through my own box of consolatory tapes, back home in the spirit of that soppy Kathy Mattea number, 'Eighteen Wheels and a Dozen Roses'; back to a woman whom I'll call Jolene (her family mythology insists that, though born years before the Dolly Parton hit, she was almost called that), who I hope is keeping the porch-light on for me.

Whoops. Maybe I've missed something out here; something which just goes to show that John is right; that you never know what's round the next corner.

Someone somewhere thinks you're a shit . . .

In retrospect it's easy to say: make sure you're sufficiently post-marital before dabbling in post-marital relationships. But once you find yourself returning to the world, the feeling that you're walking unaided hides from you the fact that you're walking on dangerous ground. Feeling, like Loretta Lynn, that you're 'Rated Ex', you want to show yourself and the world that you can still do it; and even if the world you wake up in after your long marital sleep has more diseases to be afraid of than the old world did, you're ten years on from the ungainly courtier you were in your pre-marriage days. You find that you can talk all of a sudden, that you're a sensitive beast, maybe, that, *Joy of Sex*-aware, you can make contact with those places that proved elusive when you were young.

But what you don't know is whether you're ready for what follows when you whip your clothes off and drop your new self into the intimacy whirlpool. Initially the feelings – the warm water on the skin, the little jets of pressure – are nice; but somewhere, if you're not ready, the thing goes cold and uncomfortable on you, and you find you can't be sure. Feeling that at this time of all times you have to be honest – for the one thing you can't do is feel that you're setting the ball rolling on the long course to another divorce – you back out, and prompt the ire of thirtysomething women worried about the tick of the biological clock; before you can say 'on the rebound' you're living proof of the myth that cuckolds take revenge on the opposite sex. Sorry, old friend whom I no longer speak to after one ill-considered leap that was followed by a fall; sorry, friends whose friend I upset. It comes as a bit of a shock; after all the florid, sympathetic tributes that come your way when your wife leaves you, you suddenly find yourself scared to open the mail in case it's one of those little boxes they advertise in *Private Eye* containing a little plastic jobby and a card reading *Someone somewhere thinks you're a shit.*

But the process is a sound one, in the end; desperate single people, with their passions and their insecurities, so scare you that you decide that you're happy to live alone; and as soon as you're happy – really happy – to live alone, then it means that you're ready and willing to take on someone's passions and insecurities. It's something about not wanting to belong to a club that will have you as a member; something about reaching the point of self-sufficiency by which you can know yourself. I'm completely sure I want to spend the rest of my life in solitude on the morning before the night I end up with my clothes off on the floor of Jolene's front room; and on the morning after the night before, when I find that I've woken up with someone lovely as well as having gone to bed with one, I'm on the way to being sure I want to spend the rest of my life with her.

Her life isn't without some business to sort out; she is another one (where do I find them?) who has a violent husband in the background of her life, and when I appear on the scene his months of non-communication disappear, and his aggression is dissolved in a sugary solution of expensive bouquets and slap-up meals. But his wishful thinking can't reverse the process his brutishness began, any more than mine could; can't fill the spaces that his silence left, any more than mine could; can't replace her knowledge that she's been in the wrong place, any more than mine could. Legality and family make her think of going back, of course, but she doesn't, and our first months pass in a mist of well-being; weekends together while she's working away, trying to forge a living from the waste of what she's been left; and, while she's away, a time to ponder on the wonder that I have now, and the wonder to which I didn't contribute before.

It's a striking time for me in all sorts of ways; full of idealistic feeling, I feel composed of endless heaps of understanding, a different person from the person who married Ruby; like John, I am determined to sort out the past by living properly in the present. Being offered not only the chance to start again, but an entirely different thing to start with, more graceful than the last, I know that it's a sacred one (she's rigorous, is Jolene, and searching in terms of how life and love interact); and I also know how much she has to work out and puzzle through before she's straight, and since my biological clock went digital long ago, I don't harry her with my ticking, and can leave her space and time to work out what I've already done; that this is right.

Above all I just feel a strong sense of what crap I must have talked when I was trying to get Ruby to stay with me; how blind I must have been to the reality of what had happened to her, to what she wanted to do. (I don't think she explained it very well, but that's another thing altogether.) Given joy, it doesn't trouble me to agree with everything she says for a while; to happily concede that she was right about x and y and z. Watching Jolene's family turn on her in a situation with far more patent rights and wrongs than Ruby's had to go on, I realize the ways that Ruby has suffered, and realize what tears she must have shed; watching the way that her husband, protected by the fact that she hasn't had him arrested for his 'bit of domestic', gets away with spreading the word that their breakdown is just an another-man-ran-off-with-my-wife routine, I realize how I propagandized the same way, how I too was a man incapable of listening to home-truths uttered by a woman at home.

Not that Ruby is satisfied with my (admittedly limited) remorse when I tell her of these things. My new relationship seems to inspire a bitterness that sits plum in contrast with my idealism. We have the Greek round needing to talk to 'that tart' or 'that bitch'; he is apparently determined that if he wasn't accepted by me then Jolene won't be by Ruby. Ruby piles round one Saturday morning to put Jolene straight on what a bastard I am and when Jolene fails to agree she accuses her of the heinous crime of 'sitting on my carpet'. There's a jealousy theme too, no doubt – Ruby has to deal with another woman potentially living closer to the bosom of the family than she does – but that doesn't assuage the disappointment I feel that even my happiness is to be tainted with the nip, tuck and fuckery of post-marital shenanigans.

But things are changed; are changed for ever; somehow, it's clear as time runs on, there's a new power in the land. One night Jolene and I come back from a week away with the children – maybe it was New Year, I can't remember – and we find no duvets on the children's beds. We think maybe Ruby has borrowed them for visitors or something, so in all innocence we ring her and ask; she tells me they're on the spare bed and I say fine. Two minutes later the phone rings; and she's ranting about how I'm accusing her. How dare I make out that she can't go into her own house if she wants? What right do I have to speak to her in that way? Me and my bitch can fuck right off . . . and I know from the tone that the Greek is there and that they're going to be at the door any minute.

But now I don't feel the need for police or anything else. Instead I say to Jolene that we will simply not respond at all; since there really is nothing to say, nothing to excuse, we'll simply refuse to talk about it, say we're tired and we're going to bed. So we do; when they burst in, we have made up a tray of goodies – French bread, pâté, a Christmas bottle of champagne – we just say goodnight, and leave them standing there, in the hall. Confused, they stay an hour, presuming, I suppose, that, freaked out, we'll come down. We don't. We drink the champagne and make a mess of crumbs on the bedsheets. They retreat in disorder in the end, making their mark before they go. But the extent of what they can do is shown in the paltriness of their demonstrations of ire: a few books taken off the shelf and 'creep' and 'arsehole' and 'all words' written next to my name; half a packet of cigarettes chucked into the dish-water; and – feeblest of all – the speaker-wires disconnected on the stereo, so that the next time I reach for a C&W LP there's just silence. And a Happy New Year to you too.

BE ALL THE WOMEN YOU WANT TO BE . . .

It's Sunday, so it's the Lost Leader at the British Legion in Fareham. And there's Pete Palmer up on stage again, and his patter is just as cringeworthy as last time; it would be, since it's just the same. 'Let's dedicate this to that little company up the road that sells power-tools.' 'It's about this time in the evening that I realize I'm not getting any younger. Twenty-two? That's my hat-size.' But there's a new direction, too. 'I'd like you all to welcome back John to the band.' He points to the drummer, a young lad with floppy hair that looks like a washed-out hair-dressing-at-home perm and who's wearing a black shirt with an extraordinary orange-flame pattern on it; it's a familiar design, a yuppie-country one, a Brooks and Dunn or someone like that design. 'Glad to have you back, John,' says Pete. 'But the shirt . . . mmm. Not so much Garth Brooks, more the three-thirty at Newmarket . . .'

I sit down with a nice couple and we talk about music for a bit; they like George Jones rather than Pete Palmer, but Pete Palmer will do to get along with. The bloke, an electrician, actually looks like George Jones, but I don't realize this until later and, in any case, I am up to here by this stage with people who think they are George Jones. Around the room are others who look like they might be someone else. It's an older set; there's a Loretta Lynn, a Coal Miner's Daughter, with black tresses added artificially to her hair; and I see my first Dolly Parton wig. 'BE ALL THE WOMEN YOU WANT TO BE', the ads in the C&W mags run, with pictures of Dolly in what I imagine is her own hair. But here the dumpy woman wearing the splurge of blonde has black hair dribbling down out the back of it, and if she's being all the women she wants to be she must have very limited ambitions.

Brucie, whom I've arranged to meet here, eventually turns up. He's a big, big man in a rebel cap and a jerkin and he walks with a limp. He has a broad, broad face and big, big-framed glasses; in fact he has a bit of Harry Secombe about him, although at the moments at which Harry breaks into that inanely goonish laughter Brucie looks like he might burst into tears at the fate of those less fortunate than himself. His tales are littered with moments when tears might come and tears might not; but his own tears have been dislocated into acts of worship of others who held tears back. As his eyes brim, it seems that he's doomed to remember the smiles on the faces of others; he retreats, gets on with his own work, suffers in silence.

About country music he has no such problems. He has boasts,

and he wants to make them. While in Italy with the army in 1949, he made friends with some American troops who had organized a phone-link to the stars back home, and Brucie got on the line and talked to Hank Williams himself; Hank, asked, played 'Howling at the Moon' back down the radio-link. Later, as a regular soldier, he walked into a NAAFI in Germany and the first person he bumped into was Merle Haggard. Now, 'Okie From Muskogee' is his song, his anthem. 'You know that one, don't you?' he asks. And he starts singing, with Pete Palmer discordantly working some oldie in the background, all the stuff about how they don't smoke marijuana or do group sex in Muskogee; how the kids, who still respect the college dean, spend the time allocated for amours 'pitching woo'.

It was while he was in the army that he began working for others, organizing country music benefit gigs. The turning-point was in Iraq in 1955. He was barracked in a garrison with a local population employed to fetch and carry for the soldiers, and one day one of the Iraqi children went out into the fields and stepped on a landmine. Bruce and his comrades went out themselves when they heard the explosion and saw the child being carried into the camp. 'All around the child the adults were screaming and wailing – the child had had a leg blown off.' Brucie's eyes begin to water. 'But the child himself – he smiled,' he insists. And the smile lived with him, and still lives with him today. He got some singers and an audience together in the mess and raised more than a £100; a tidy sum in the mid-fifties.

And so on, and so on. He came out the army and set up the Southern Comancheros, a club down on the south coast; he booked bands, ran shows, raised money for charity – 'for those less fortunate'. He had a bronze eagle cast and it was sent round country clubs, awarded as a gong to charitable sorts who did the most for others. By the time it was returned to him, years later, forty-odd thousand pounds had been raised. Meanwhile, he took to driving the big rigs and embraced all the trappings of the country trucker. 'I had the CB radio,' he says, 'and my handle was Maverick. And I had the Confederate flags on the dashboard.' He loved the road life – the truck-stops, the lay-bys, the cafés – the places where he would pull up, and by the time he'd locked up, a plate of what he wanted would be ready on the table for him. 'But that's a dead scene now,' he says. 'All Little Chefs. Little Chefs won't let truckers in. It's not because of problems with truckers. It's because the customers don't like the smell of diesel. They can stand those blueberry pancakes all right . . .'

The Lost Leader crowd are getting down to it and Bruce says that if his wife was here he would be up there, that he still gets around the floor. But he's holding out one leg, stiff, in front of him, and he tells me a tale straight from Red Sovine, those 'Big Joe and Phantom 309' songs. One day he took out a rig with a load of scrap-metal, maybe a skip, on the back. Somewhere on the lost highway he lost the place with it, and the load – he uses technical terms I can't understand – swayed and twisted and went over; went over on top of him. But the hardest bit was not the injury, but the insult. For, out of hospital, he was dumped; within a month, he says, he'd had papers from the DVLC disqualifying him from further driving and leaving him high and dry, off the road once and for all.

The tears threaten again, and so he pulls out pictures of himself from a file. Himself with his children, Wayne (named after the Duke) and Lorayne (spelt to homogenize with Wayne). Himself profiled in *Southern Country* magazine for raising such and such an amount for such and such a charity. Himself in Union blue at a fund-raiser. Himself as president of CHAT, a toys-for-hospitals charity, distributing largesse. Himself organizing a benefit for Stephanie, a local girl who went to sleep on Christmas Eve with two legs and woke up in hospital the next day with none after a meningitis-linked amputation. The thought of her hits him and his eyes fill again, but then he catches hold of the memory of being taken into the ward to meet the girl herself. 'You go through your life and you think you've met happy people,' he says, 'but let me tell you, you haven't seen the smile on the face of that girl . . .'

And the work never stops, for when Pete Palmer comes over and sits down at break-time, Brucie produces the text of a lullaby that Stephanie's father wrote for her while she was sleeping off her anaesthetic, and Pete agrees – readily and decently – to do an arrangement so that Bruce or someone else can perform a country version of it at a big fund-raiser they're having later in the year. I look around. The band are having their tea-break. Pete is in his off-duty blue woolly, and his wife, called in at the last minute to be his sound-man, is sitting miserably by the console. 'Life,' says Bruce, as he hands me the lullaby, photo-copied from the *Daily Mirror*, to read. 'Country music's about life. People who think it's miserable don't know anything about life.' And I notice that John, the drummer, the man who's just come back from hospital, and who Pete has back in his band, and who's been banging the skins all evening, is missing an arm. He's been in hospital having lost it in a crash. And – of course – he's smiling.

There's always one teddy that makes you say, 'That's the one . . .'

The High Chapparal – the version that meets weekly at Short's Club, just a stone's throw from the paras' base at Holywood in Belfast – has its own Big John. 'I'd've wore my brown suit if I'd'a known you were coming,' Sam says, and it's easy to see that in brown he would be a dead ringer for the big daddy from the big daddy of all western TV serials.

Sam's a large man, and a larger-than-life one as well. He walks about the smart, glossy club with a word for everyone. But not just that; his words come either in broad Belfast brogue – rich enough for most days, one would have thought – or in a rich, part-southern, part-western drawl, pitched somewhere between John Wayne and Blanche DuBois. Jolene is with me tonight, along for the ride, and he kisses her: 'You're as purtee as the furst flower o' th' morning by the light o' th' prairie dawn.' It's a glowing testimony, though it's somewhat undermined when we learn he's due into the ophthalmic ward of the Royal Belfast the following Wednesday. Having delivered his kiss, Sam turns away and practically bumps into a table.

He's still at it later in the evening when I come across him outside the toilets, and even talking about himself, in private, he can't quite stop himself from lapsing into performance. Like Brucie, he's a disabled trucker; he kept driving through four heart attacks and a heart op, but his eyes have finally done for him, like the last of the fourteen swords that brought down Bluebeard. Like Brucie, he uses his club to make money for charity; not just general charities, but specific, individual acts of mercy. 'Just de-termined to do somethin' for those ley-ss fortunate than my-self,' he says. He was walking round the club one night and saw a member in tears: 'One of the girls,' says Sam, 'so I asked her what was the matter. She says, "I'm sorry, Sam, I'm just thinking of my little niece."' The niece went too near the fire in a nylon nightie; Sam spares me the details, though he's faced them down, and having faced them, got to work and raised £1,000 through shootouts. 'The girl's coming to get the cheque next month,' says Sam. 'And if she wants to blow it all in one go, head for EuroDisney the month after, that's up to her. The money's for her.'

But this is nothing compared with how it all started. 'One day, when ah was still drivin',' says Sam, 'ah pulled my rig into a truck-stop.' (He does say this, honestly.) 'And ah'm having my tea' – he's not without irony here – 'and readin' the paper, and ah see a story of a girl who's had fo-wer liver trans-plants. But her body keeps rejectin' them, y'see? Now, ah don't know anything 'bout the girl; all it says is she's in Addenbrooke's Hospital, over in London. Or Cambridge, is it? So ah pull my rig over' – to the side of the road? – 'right outside the flower-shop, the Interflora place, and ah park outside; ah just pull the lorry up outside the florist's. Ah go in and ah say, ah say' – it's impossible to stop Foghorn and Leghorn creeping into your head – '"ah want you to send some flowers to this place, a pur-ty bou-quet to this hospital." And the woman says, "How much do you want to spend?" And ah say, "It's not so much how much ah want to spend, but how big can you make it?"'

'So she's getting that sorted out. And as she's doing that, ah look round at this shelf and there's all these teddies. And you know with teddies' – this is coming from a man who is about six-foot-six and built like a brick shithouse – 'with teddies, you look round and there's always one teddy that makes you say, "That's the one." So ah say, "Get me that teddy." And she pulls this teddy down, and she looks in the ear for the code, and she rings the shop in London and she says, "That's fine, they've got that teddy – the only problem is that that teddy costs thirty-six pounds." And ah say, "Ah don't care if it costs a hundred and thirty-six; she's having that teddy."' Of course, anyone with a modicum of country knowledge can't help but think of 'Teddy Bear', that talkie-weepie, also by Red Sovine, in which the fatherless crippled child sits at home making calls on the CB in the name of Teddy Bear, and all the trucks in the world come up his cul-de-sac offering to give him a ride. But Sam is not sloshy like that; nor is he boastful, though he is proud. But, most obviously, he's as unsentimental as it's possible to be while being moved by others' plight.

'A few weeks later ah get a call from a girl ah know who works on the *Belfast Telegraph*, a girl called June. Ah always say to her, there's only one Ju-ly, but there's plenty Junes. And she tells me the mother wants to know who's sending the flowers, so I arrange to talk to her on the phone. Now the wee girl's just rejected the fourth liver, so she's in a bad way, and the mother says, "She's very poorly." I says, "Can you come over here and just bring her for half an hour to the club? I'll get you taxis here, taxis there . . ." And the mother says, "I think she'd like that." Now I've got a photo of that girl sitting here in this club with my big white stetson on. And she's all yellow from the jaundice. But there's a smile there –'

What is it about big, disabled truck-drivers and the smiles on the faces of children? But Sam is not Brucie after all, because there are no tears there, there's not the same worry behind the bluster. 'Three weeks later,' says Sam unflatly, 'she was dead. But we all felt we'd done something . . .' No, Sam is not Brucie. Sam is a big, happy man; though he sings, too, at charity dos. The tale over, he begins performing there, outside the toilets, talking me through his patter. 'I always get up on stage and try and do a wee bit with the audience, you know. I say, "I'm an old trucker. Any other old truckers here?" And I point down to a woman at the front and I say, "Excuse me, ma'am, I think you misread my lips – I said *truckers*." And then I say, "My wife knows I'm just an old trucker, and" – I point to the same woman – "by the way, my wife agrees with what you thought I said." That kind of thing,' Sam says, 'it kinda gits them going.' He thinks for a moment, but only a moment: 'Or I say, "Any Merle Haggard fans here?" They all cheer. I say, "Sorry, he can't make it. But he rang me up and he says, 'Sam, I'm sorry I can't be with you, but here's a song – you sing it for them.'" And that's me off – I give them a song.'

We talk for a bit about trucking, about why country music and trucking go together. His voice moves up a gear again, and he starts to perform again, but there's conviction in him as he lays it on: 'One of my favourite songs,' he says, 'is "Ain't It Good to be Back Home Again". When I first heard that, I thought, "That's a trucker's song, that is."' He sings one of the stanzas in a rough, deep, a cappella, kind of beautiful way; it's about the homeward journey, the whine of the wheels, the smooth downhill slide towards a night sleeping in one's own bed after a week on the road. 'Where you from?' he asks me. I say, 'Glasgow; once upon a time, anyway.' He says, 'I don't know about Glasgow, but have you ever noticed how all towns are in valleys?' He's obviously never been to the Fens, someone says when I get home, but on the spur of the moment I can't be sure it's not true. He sings the stanza again, and begins to improvise; his drawl and his natural voice have somehow synthesized; it's mid-Atlantic, but in a schizoid, not a bland sense. 'You've been away two weeks,' he says, 'and you're getting near your home-town – so near you actually begin to feel it, to feel it's near. You come up a hill and over it, and you see the street-lights on, the lights of your old home-town. And as you see it, you hear the whine of the wheels and the moan of the engine, and instead of it sounding lonely, like it's been sounding all these days, it sounds fine. And you push your back into your seat and stretch your arms out and you let a big sigh out – and it's just what that song says: "Ain't It Good to be Back Home Again" . . .'

CHAPTER SIX

The Code of the West Ain't No Words on a Page

Anyone for a nice cup of tea?

JB's buckskin backside is on the seat, and his cowboy-booted feet are up on the desk, as if he owns the place, or as if he's the sheriff of this city. Of course he does own the place (Silver City is part of his Spirit of the West park) and if he's sheriff he's also marshal, jailer, saloon-owner, food-storekeeper, ostler, museum-curator, pan-handler, gold-weigher, fish-stock-watcher, caterer and a host of other practical occupations. JB – the initials are those of James Butler Hickock, aka Wild Bill – is a hands-on, busy man.

He tells me about a call he had from Los Angeles, when Spirit of the West was still called Frontier City and was still up in Hungerford, in the days when Hungerford, pre-Michael Ryan, still had a taste for Wild West shootouts. (He has since uprooted it and moved it out west, where it is now; 'lock, stock and barrel' applies literally, since JB has, among other things, a valuable collection of Wild West gunware.) The call was from the producer of an American TV programme called *You Asked For It*, which JB reckons is not unlike *Jim'll Fix It*, except that the programme was less of a wish factory, more of an inquiry bureau. Someone had written in in classic 'please settle a family argument' style: 'My brother says there are cowboys in England and I don't believe him.' The producer wanted to send a crew down to Frontier City and do some filming of JB and his friends to prove the brother right.

JB was 'happy to oblige'. He twangs this sentence with a twang half-American and half-Wiltshire, and lights up a cheroot. The crew arrived, filmed JB and his cowboy cronies walking round JB's city in full Wild West wear and went off 'happy with what they had in the can'. But a couple of weeks later JB got another call. Because of the authenticity of Frontier City – the sheriff's office, the jail, the saloon, all built in authentic log-and-clapboard – there had been nothing to prove that they were in fact in England; when they'd run the tape on the programme, all people saw was a posse of cowboys in a Wild West town, and it could have been in Colorado or Montana or Arizona or New Mexico.

So the crew came back to Frontier City, Hungerford, and shot the sequence again. But this time the instructions were more specific. The backdrop was shifted to the local stately pile. JB, once again in full Buffalo Bill regalia, was asked to come out the grand front door, walk down the stairs to the rose-garden, where his compadres would be waiting in their chaps. He was given a script as well as marching-orders. What he *wasn't* to say was, 'Howdy, pardner' or any of his other Frontier City greetings; what he had to say was, 'Good morning chaps,' and, in the plummiest Ealing tones possible, 'Anyone for a nice cup of tea?'

As the LA crew departed, the director turned to JB: 'Now they'll have to believe there are cowboys in England.'

I liked cowboys and Indians. When I was eleven . . .

Cowboys in England there are; not that Roy cares. 'We always finish at eleven; you get in at eleven-thirty; I make a cup of tea, the wife makes a sandwich. In bed by midnight. What else would you do on a Sunday night?' Lazy Dog, whose lead singer looks like Dwight Yoakam crossed with a young Bjorn Borg, are playing a rocky, Flatlander-esque third set at the Morris Motors club in Oxford. Roy, who organizes it, is not a westerner; he books country bands every week, but he wears a leather jacket, an M&S woolly and a pair of ornery trousers. He doesn't seem to dance, but sits with his wife and nurses a beer shandy. There are some spectacular dancers on the floor of his club, including a couple who, Nike Air-style, have red lights fitted into their boot heels which flash on and off when their crocodiling legs make contact with the floor.

Roy's club is in Cowley, in the shade of what used to be the British Leyland factory, and he himself has worked on the truck production line most of his life. He quite likes car songs – he quotes the Johnny Cash number, 'One Piece at a Time' – but not especially. He came to country via rock and roll, just like Johnny Cash did, when Cash and Carl Perkins were together on the Sun record label. Johnnie Horton and Frankie Laine and Marty Robbins brought him over to country, but he can't stand the way westerners have 'assumed' country. 'You get young 'uns in,' he says, 'and they just laugh at people dressed up. It's bringing down the music I love.'

He tells a story of a man who came in in spurs, and, line-dancing, kicked his heel back and sliced open a woman's leg. Since then, if he sees anyone in spurs on the dance-floor, he threatens to turn the lights on and stop the music. So though there are cowboys in the club – he points out the Thatcham Cowboy, a photographer from Newbury, and a man called Mick who drinks orange juice and Coke mixed and calls it Mississippi Mud – Roy is not keen on them, and the bulk of the house are Sunday-night dancers in shirts and ties and sensible frocks.

'Don't get me wrong,' says Roy. 'I liked cowboys and Indians. When I was eleven.' On the way out I see a photo of him on the committee members' board. It turns out his name is Winchester.

***People like to look at you, but they don't want to look
like you . . .***

Cowboys there are in England, and Indians too. At first glance,
Roy – another Roy – is the sort of Indian who gives westerners
a bad name. Fair enough – he's dressed as an Indian from top
to toe, from horny headpiece to moccasin soles. His skin has
been darkened with Pan-stick-y browning (does Max Factor
make a shade called *Native* American Tan?) and in black and
white on his cheek and nose are two stripes that run diagonally
across one eye. But busy as he is selling raffle-tickets on the
door of the Buffalo Club in Hampshire, he needs his specs, so he
has them on, and they're silver-rimmed, thick reading-frames,
£59.99 from Boots the Chemist, a sort rarely seen on the Apache
warpath. It being deep midwinter, he also has peeping out above
his beautiful, beaded moccasins, a pair of beige socks, £2.99
from C&A, which somehow break the illusion that Roy could
creep through a forest and make tracks on a deer without breaking a twig. And spinning the discs on the interval disco and
making that combine with M C-ing the three sets Memphis
Roots are playing tonight – well, of course he needs a watch,
just like the Centurion in *The Greatest Story Ever Told* or *Ben
Hur* or whichever film it is that features the part of General
Anachronistus.

Well, maybe it's just anachronism; maybe it's shambolism.
But at the same time, about his person, and about that of
Irene, his wife, there are many, many beautiful things. Irene,
especially, wears a lot of turquoise jewellery; they're in Navajo
designs and Navajo colours, and her silver rings, interlinked,
run exotically up her swarthy arm. She has an eye for colours
and wears nice ones; she has stuff at home that's sensational,
Roy says, especially an Indian dress made of skin and beadwork
that took her a year to construct and weighs ten pounds. She
has a thick black pony-tail drawn round the side of her foxy,

bright face; it looks like an authentic style. Roy also has long hair, a double dose, for it's clear that his head-dress features hair that is not his own; though when he pulls off the black pony-tail that goes with the headgear he has another, identical, in grey underneath.

Roy is obsessed with Indians, he tells us as we sit in the lobby of the Community School eating chickenburger in a basket, and the Indian reconstructions he and his mates do are his life, or have been since he was invalided out of the Milk Marketing Board, for whom he used to drive milk-tankers around the south coast farmlands. Tonight no one else is wearing Indian stuff, except a man called Blackjack, an odd, thin-faced man with a roguish air, who comes later. But through the year they have special Indian theme evenings, and there are others that wear the clobber then. He talks me through his full regalia. His hat is a half-bonnet, half-way between the two extremes possible, half-way from a single feather to a full chief's head-dress. His half-bonnet has a white furry bit, a feather crown, red beads; it also has medicine-man horns, which Roy is proud of: 'Often the medicine-man was the real chief – the real Indian chief bowed to the medicine-man, was scared of the medicine-man.'

Indians? Medicine-men? Isn't Roy due a PC injection? But it turns out that his obsession isn't a lifelong one. He was running a cowboy club based in a C&W club in Portsmouth, and when interest dropped, becoming Indians was pretty much just a strategy to keep the club going. They got hold of three tepees, practised Indian dances and took them to the Brean Sands Pontin's, in Devon, where they met Dick and Geneva, the American couple credited with introducing line-dancing to Britain. Inspired, Roy and Irene formed the Buffalo to bring in the dancers and give the Indian group a lift. So now there are about twenty-five Indians in their group; a pretty small yield, actually, since the Buffalo is heaving with people line-dancing in their huge, orderly queues. 'It's a constant struggle to get more people involved in the Indian side of things,' says Roy. 'A lot of people like to look at you, but they don't want to take that little extra step and look like you,' he adds, wist filling him up to the head-dress.

So the merry band that goes off in the tepees for the holidays is a thinnish crowd, though they meet other groups and have pow-wows. Their speciality – and a great favourite at school fêtes – is their range of dances. There's the Hoop Dance. 'That was a competition, you know, between the young braves.' He describes it in detail, incomprehensibly. 'Then there's the Buffalo Dance. They did that when they had killed a buffalo – it sort of atoned for the buffalo's spirit. They did that even though they never wasted any bit of the buffalo; it was all killed for a reason.' He describes it in detail, incomprehensibly. And of course there is the Rain Dance, complete with its *de rigueur* ending: 'Well, we were performing one weekend, can't remember where. We do three sets a day and we like to vary them, so we didn't put in the Rain Dance until the end. Well, not a cloud in the sky all day, while we were doing the Hoop Dance and the Buffalo Dance, but as soon as we'd finished the Rain Dance, well, blow me but didn't the heavens open . . .' It was amazing, he says, but his face says that he wasn't amazed in a spiritual sense – '. . . well, the crowd just loved it,' he says, when pushed. I ask if he's interested in any of the history, the philosophy, and he looks baffled, bemused. 'The religion – well, that *can* get a bit heavy. No, what I like is the dressing-up and the dancing.'

The last I see of him, he's leading the Trilogy, the ceremonial end to the night they have in clubs where there is western dressing-up. For the Trilogy the band or the disco plays the 'American Trilogy', the old Elvis 'Glory Glory' thing, and the westerners parade in with their flags and banners. They make a huge circle around the edge of the hall, and at stately moments in the song raise or lower or hold out their flags; and then, at the end, the Confederate dead are fêted when everyone lets off their guns in a volley. In most places it's a ceremony religiously observed; but here at the Buffalo, most of the members, particularly the line-dancers, sit on their backsides, and poor old Roy is left to lead a rather pathetic line of plain-clothesers around the floor.

'The Indian Cowboy'

Cowboys in England there are, and there are general stores of a very specific nature where they go to get dressed up. They're all over the country, though few of the trading-posts are, like the one in Hounslow, run by the Indians. (We're talking sub-continental, not cowboys-and-, of course.) Chadha's store, West-star, with Country FM blaring out on the in-store stereo, is awash with most of the things an aspiring cowpoke might need. Here you get the buckskin jackets, the cattleman western shirts with embroidered Confederate flag motifs, the leather waist-coats; there are stetsons, ten-gallon hats, and racks and racks of shoelace ties; and for about £90 you can have a full Indian head-dress, albeit a slightly home-made-looking off-yellow number.

It's not just clothes, of course; the real fiends have houses full of paraphernalia, and here you can get some of it, from General Custer toby jugs to throwing knives, from tomahawks to John Wayne photographs, from Civil War replica caps to Last Rebel-brand cigarette papers. It's an odd mish-mash of the politically acceptable and the utterly unacceptable. 'Ride to Live, Live to Ride', says a bucking-bronco belt-buckle, pretty much neutrally; an Indian pow-wow T-shirt offers, acceptably, 'Invaded But Not Conquered'; but what are we to make of 'If Guns Are Outlawed, Only Outlaws Will Have Guns', available for bumpersticking? Chadha's wife has no real answer to the question of why they keep so vividly a redneck item; all she'll say is that her husband is a well-known figure in the C&W world, and if there were racist reactions when they first bought the store, when they first went out on the road to festivals, well, they no longer get them now.

Needless to say, the JBs and the Roys of this world have western stuff which is in a different category, stuff found only in collections or antique-shops – the chaps, the oil-skin coats, the original saddles. Weststar is firmly for the punters, is firmly in the real, the retail world. Yet Chadha, his wife says, was 'really into' the western scene before they met and before they bought the shop; for him it's more than a business. 'The Indian Cowboy'? I wonder, thinking of the man in the Joe Ely song who saves the circus by lassooing the wild horses who are threatening to stampede the elephants; the man who, as an outsider, gets little thanks for his pains and his work and his skill.

We've a nice town here. We like to keep it clean...

Cowboys in England there are, and there are Outlaws in Suffolk; they meet once a week, in Sudbury, advertised in the local press, so they're hardly the Hole in the Wall gang and hardly hard to find; but I still manage not to find them. I've got the day wrong and the Suffolk Outlaws meet tomorrow, so (a) I don't suppose I would get a job with Pinkerton's, the detectives who always ended up chasing Hannibal and Kid in *Alias Smith and Jones*; and (b) I wind up at the Ponderosa Club, in the Portakabin social club belonging to Stowmarket Football Club.

The compère is John, a sweet old bloke on post-heart attack crutches. He's not a cowboy, but he has the shiny silver *Keep It Country* bowling blouson over his tan slacks. He's been booking acts for the club for many years, having learnt the art of promotion in The Gambia, where he was a soldier, when he hired up 'a couple of darkie boys on the beach' to come and play gigs 'for peanuts' – leftovers from the officers' table – in the mess. Busy, he fobs me off on a short man called Adrian, a technician with the BT labs at Ipswich. He has a thin, wiry moustache sitting under a seventies bouffant – it's Tennessee Ernie Ford meets Gilbert O'Sullivan – and we talk amiably for a bit about

161

music until a slow one comes on and someone he says is his sister-in-law hoves into view and he says he's off to 'grab a grope'.

I sit watching the singers for a while. It's a double-header tonight; there's a local pub duo called A Touch of Country – which makes C&W sound more like a curse than a blessing – and a well-known Essex boy called Dane Stevens. Dane has those high, dimpled cheekbones Cliff Richard has, a blue silky shirt, a bouffant even bigger than Adrian's and an *it's that time of the night* showbiz manner that means that no matter how lonesome the song claims he is, it won't go by without a cheesy smile. 'If you're in love, look into each other's eyes,' he says, and the fans love him; and though I am, I'm alone again on the road tonight, so I don't. There's a slight hillbilly flavour in the room; as well as John dancing around on his crutches, there's a couple of thin, slack-jawed yokelish blokes in thick specs dominating; when they're not doing flagellatory bum-whipping routines to a song called 'I Ride a Horse', they're whooping train-whistles in the choruses of the Johnny Cash numbers. They look let out, like they've come down from the Blue Ridge mountains, like they might be suffering from cabin fever.

But there are no mountains. Neither is this Tombstone, but the Stowmarket Ponderosa has its own Wild West-style lawmaker, for Marilyn, the mayor of the town, is taking the money at the door wearing a checked shirt and her chain of office. She just smiles when I ask her if she's come to clean up the town: 'We've a nice town here,' she says loyally, replacing her cowboy hat with her Tourist Board one. I take a plainer tack; do the problems concern keeping the young people in the town? 'Keeping them here?' she says. 'It's keeping them out that's the problem.' (Two rural problems collide; you keep the youth in the town and they lager-lout all over it.) And then there's the real baddy, the sitting Tory MP, whom Marilyn wants to drive out of town at the next election. But what about those Outlaws hiding in their Hole in the Wall down the road? 'Oh, we don't have to worry about them,' she says. As I leave she has her hands in the air, clapping and singing along to Dane Stevens. Sad to say, it's a Raymond Froggatt number, but Dane Stevens's repertoire doesn't run to Singing Cowboy numbers.

I thought Gene Autry was a girl . . .

The woman who runs the bed and breakfast in Carrickfergus is not a C&W fan, but she does remember playing cowboys and Indians as a child in Belfast. 'I used to play with the boys,' she says, 'and I would always be Gene Autry. But the thing was, I'd never seen Gene Autry. And because of the name – well, I thought Gene Autry was a girl. That's why I chose him . . .'

If only Gene had kept his real name, Orvon. But it's not very cowboy-like, is it? Not exactly a name to leave you sitting tall in the saddle, and tall you need to be to admit to a liking for the Singing Cowboy numbers that Gene pioneered. It's kind of sad that in recent years 'country' has had such a strong, embarrassed urge to break itself off from 'western'. Not that I'm not embarrassed myself when I listen to Frankie Laine, with all those bull-whips and yee-hars on *Rawhide* and *Mule Train*. (Those yee-hars have left a legacy, an image of C&W listeners every bit as pervasively false as the notion that C&W-ers must be suicidal.) But go a little further back, to Gene and to Roy Rogers and – especially – to Tex Ritter, and you have something rather lovely, in a funny sort of way; something a bit silly, but a bit romantic, too; something happy and wordy and idealistic; something nicer than John Wayne-style macho antics to tell you why grown men have dressing-up boxes.

Gene started it all, if you leave out John Lomax, the folklorist who, in 1908, collected the songs that defined the cowboy as a lonesome songster, and Jimmie Rodgers, who taught the world how to yodel. Gene was just a normal hillbilly singer doing sentimental numbers – 'That Silver-Haired Daddy of Mine', to name but all – when, in spite of having no cowboy connections at all, he began to appear in horse operas, the thirties films and shows that practically created the figure of the good guy in white, invulnerable in his western shirt and wing-tips, able, like Orpheus, to soothe any savage, bristled beast with a few chords on the guitar delivered from horseback. In Autry's case the horse was Champion, the third of whom – it's disappointing to discover that there was more than one Wonder Horse – died in 1991, aged forty-two.

By the time Autry went off to World War Two, his influence had dictated that western wear had taken over from hillbilly accoutrements as the key fashion style of country music. By the time Autry came back, Roy Rogers had taken over as cowboy songster supreme. Roy (or Leonard, as he was christened, in a place called Duck Run) had no more cowboy connections than Autry had, but he too took to stetsons like a duck-run to water, first backing Autry on 'Tumbling Tumbleweed', then, when Autry went away, forming the Sons of the Pioneers, who hit the high notes with that great chimes-of-freedom number, 'Don't Fence Me In'. The Rogers image is an eternal one: 'When my time comes,' he said, 'just skin me and put me right up there on Trigger, just as if nothing had ever changed.' They didn't do it to Roy, though they did do it to Trigger; he is extant yet, stuffed and on display in the Roy Rogers Museum in Victorville, California.

But Gene and Roy were mere actors compared to Tex Ritter. In spite of being called Woodward, Tex was at least in part a true cowboy, raised on a ranch that had been in the family since 1830 and had belonged to his great-grandfather. He was studying law at the University of Texas when he began to come across western songs, and he travelled to New York and sang them on Broadway during theatrical scene changes. (The play was *Green Grow the Lilacs*, which, when musicalized, became *Oklahoma*.) On the back of his success, Tex went both east and west. In the east he gave lecture tours, performing and talking about authentic western music; in the west he made bad movies in Hollywood – he worked on the original *Lone Ranger* series, incidentally – until *High Noon* came along and Fred Zinnemann asked him to sing the theme.

And *High Noon* – the 'Do Not Forsake Me, O My Darling' one – is the Real McCoy, and not just because after *High Noon* every western had a song; it's the Real McCoy because what with *Oh to be caught 'twixt love and duty* and other expressions of antique and literate honour, the song puts you in touch with that chivalric spirit that encourages grown men to run around spouting those precepts which they glorify as the Code of the West, even though the west as they know it and are evoking it – the west they saw in Hollywood movies – never really existed. It's beautiful and lost, that spirit, but it's still noble, when held against much of what happens in Nashville, whose image-makers want the cowboys out. But if country music is really so keen on getting rid of its western appendage – well, why does every new country artiste who needs kitting out stop off at the ten-gallon-hat shop first?

If you want to come in, come in. If you don't, piss off...

I remember hearing Roger Miller make fun of the idea of the Code of the West once, singing something tongue-in-cheek melodramatic about it being no words on a page, but just something known naturally as coming-of-age; something about eating when you're hungry and drinking when you're dry and looking every man in the eye. In *Round-Up*, the magazine of the British Westerners' Association, in an obituary for a celebrated London westerner called Roy Montana, the Code of the West runs slightly differently. 'In the old west, a man's word was his bond, and people were accepted at face value, for what they were. Women were treated with respect, even the "soiled doves". You never asked a person where they were from, or where they were going.'

In fact it's me who's doing the asking when I come to the Essex village of Geftingthorpe, lost on the trail of Trailsend, a Wild West town belonging to a man called Chuck. The expensively dressed women coming out of the Sunday morning churchhouse know where it is – 'You mean the cowboy place?' – and so does the man washing his BMW and the other mending the guttering on a pretty, vine-clad cottage. That's not to say it's easy to find. After much to-ing and fro-ing and direction-taking you take a road with a dead-end sign, you wind past the top-of-the-hill smart house and you bump over half a mile of tree-lined pot-hole. In the car-park there's a collection of Confederate flag-toting American cars; you obviously need to be a Duke of Hazzard to drive there fast. My van makes it in the end, but the creaks suggest that I'd have been better off with one of the bull bar-clad Ford Maverick 4x4s the local bourgeoisie use to get to Sainsbury's.

Trailsend is a Hole in the Wall, and Chuck has a gang to go with it, a bunch of cowboys formerly known as the Missouri Raiders, now known as the Southern Hellraisers, who spend their Sundays putting nails in the walls of Trailsend or practising their charity fund-raising shootouts. When I get there, they're sitting in a row, on chairs ranged along a clapboard balcony, booted feet up on the horse-rail, sipping strong tea brewed over an open fire. There's Del, Chuck's right-hand man, factory-hand by week, stetsonned dead-eye by weekend. There's Tex, a long-distance trucker who, in black leather waistcoat, does a passable Clint Eastwood, all thin lips and pinched cheekbones. There's Colin, a jeansy long-haired smiler whose kids roam free, hiding, and another bloke who has to leave early to pack supermarket shelves.

Chuck himself is not yet dressed; his white hair is tied under a baseball cap. He shows me that he's wearing a watch. 'I'll get fined for that,' he says. 'Watches stay in the car-park.' Trailsend is thirteen years old, Chuck says, built from scratch on this hilltop piece of land bought cheap. Having established right of way by proving that there had once been a potter's cottage there, he found a map of Bodie in a history book, and got to work on copying that. 'It's authentic,' he says, 'built from scraps we dragged up here. Just like in the west. Pallets, bits of old wood. When the settlers arrived, they didn't bring the sort of materials you see in Hollywood westerns. They used whatever they could lay their hands on. And that's what we did; we built it from bits and pieces.'

Del takes me round, and it is a bit rough; the boards creak and threaten to snap underfoot, and when the wind blows on this blasty spring morning his brow furrows in an alert sort of way as if a roof might come down on our heads. The buildings lie in a shaky triangle around a patch of rough grass, sign-painted by hand to signify their use; there is a blacksmith's, a furrier, a trading post; a saloon, a barber, a livery stable. Some-one has a dicky sense of humour: DOUG GRAVES – UNDER-TAKER, reads one, while the newspaper proprietor is called I. M. A. GOSSIP. The church bell is an old tin bucket painted gold, and inside the buildings the same spare-part philosophy applies. A fireguard stuck on a counter makes a bank-clerk's grille, and someone has got hold of a load of old mannequins to play the non-speaking parts in this tale of the old west; a plastic-bald head peeps out from under the grey blanket lying on the bed in the marshal's cells, while the preacher stands pertly with one knee demurely bent, toes pointing at the floor the better to show off a bit of exotic lingerie in some Debenham's of the past. 'It's a lady preacher,' Del mutters, *sotto voce*, more in shame than out of respect for the cloth, though he smiles.

Chuck joins us as we walk up from the gold-mine. 'Y'see, I'd always dreamed of having my own bit of land,' he says. 'My own town.' The fantasy had begun when he opted out of rock 'n' roll and into the western ballads of Frankie Laine and Marty Robbins. 'They gave me a vision, those songs – "El Paso", "The

Last Gunfighter Ballad". They gave a vision of a way of living a life that I liked. And even if you can't live it all day, even if the way of the world says you can't live it every day – well, if you can get a chance at your dream, sometime in your life, isn't that something worth going for?' We walk back to where we started, the boots go back on to the horse-rail and Del's wife brings another cup of good, strong tea. 'I can put my feet up on this balcony,' Chuck says, 'and I can look around, and it's all mine. And how many people can say that? Can truly say that, about where they are, with the mortgage and the banks and the bills to pay?'

Possession has not been easy; the local new-money nobbery, with a watchful eye on property prices and a preference for Sundays without the distant rattle of re-enactment gunfire, have tried with all their might and main to move the Hellraisers on. It started with attempts to buy them out; the neighbours sent an agent to offer a named price. Chuck, responding, said that £100 more would do it. They hummed and hawed, but eventually came back with the extra hundred. Chuck, responding, said that time had passed, that the old price no longer applied, but that £100 more would do it. 'They came back three times before they twigged,' he says, 'that it would always be £100 more than they offered.' Another neighbour on the other side asked him to name his price. '"A million," I said. He said, "Don't be ridiculous," and I said, "Well, what price do you put on a dream?" And even if he'd offered a million – well, the price would always have been £100 more.'

So some of the villagers, Chuck claims, tried different tacks. First they argued about the boundaries. 'It got to the point where they were arguing with us about half a tree,' says Chuck. The boundary between one piece of land and another was a ridge, and one day one of the Trailsend children was seen standing on the ridge and picking up a twig from the other side; an accusation of theft followed. Extending the principle, they began to accuse them of other things. As a result of Trailsend's open-door policy

– 'I always say, "If you want to come in, come in. If you don't, piss off"' – local children came to play there, and suggestions were made that the Trailsenders were enticing children for nefarious purposes. Other malicious reports followed, with the police called in; they were accused of owning unlicensed fire-arms, of serving unlicensed drinks, of dealing in drugs. 'After the first time, the police knew what whoever was reporting us was up to. So they would come up here, have a chat and a cup of tea, then look at their watches. "Right, that's half an hour," they'd say. "They've seen us arrive and they'll see us go. So there's nothing to worry about, for us or for you . . ."'

Of course, all pioneers need some Indians lurking in the shrubbery to inflate the value of their dreams; while I'm there I sense no hostility, and Chuck admits that, what with planners and police happy with what's going on in Trailsend, there's something like peace now; give or take the odd bit of yobbo vandalism, the odd night-time intrusion, things are quiet. What he has to say about the people living round about is mainly an assertion of his own values: 'They're worried about what their houses are worth, I suppose. Yet you'd think for a buyer that having something special in their backyard would be exciting, an addition, not a cause for resentment. I think,' he says, generally, 'people just can't bear to see anyone do anything *different*. If what we chose to do up here was, say, hitting a little white ball into a hole with a big stupid stick, they'd be happy as Larry. But because of how we choose to spend our time – maybe on a Sunday we'll divide into two, and one group tries to take the town from the other – we get lumbered with a load of nonsense. But all we want to do is live in peace . . .'

Gunfire peppers the air as I wander back to the van. Over in the corner, by the made-up church, there's a little graveyard. It looks like a pet cemetery in someone's garden for a minute, but it's not that; and I'm shocked, though not surprised, to see that the graves there are real. There's a weathered hand-painted block of white wood with the legend J A K E – 1925–1987. Chuck comes over. 'He was one of the Raiders. He wanted to be buried up here, but the family didn't like it, and they had him cremated over in Chelmsford. So we put some of his bits and pieces in – his hat, his gun – and buried those instead.' But another 'stone' (JOHN MANN – BIG BAD JOHN – 1920–1993) is surrounded by those big floral tributes they love in the East End, words – DAD and GRANDPA – in capital letters built out of flowers. '*He*'s here,' says Chuck, sipping his tea. In the shade of the gallows, Big Bad John's ashes lie. GONE TO THE RIDING HERD IN THE SKY, says the legend. RIDE IN PEACE.

Any Mexicans in here tonight?

At Fort San Antone, near Preston, a bunch of likeable scousers called the Joe Piper Band are about to play Jimmy Buffett's 'Margaritaville'. 'Any Mexicans in here tonight?' asks the bassist, and he looks at his watch. ''Cos if there are they've just missed the last bus home.' There aren't any Mexicans but there are some Northern Irish; a busload from the Blazing Saddles Club in Belfast are having their weekend away, and, to my amazement, sitting there are some people I met when I was over there; Big Sam is not there, but Jackie is there with his wife Audrey, and Agnes is there, and fifty others who've put away a fiver a week over the last year to break the back of the cost of their annual tour.

The outside of Fort San Antone is built out of tall logs, designed like a toy cavalry fort you might have had for your sixth birthday, yet fifteen feet high, with guard emplacements at the corners and a big gateway with two tattered flags flying. VISIT A LITTLE PIECE OF AMERICA THAT HAS BEEN IN YOUR DREAMS SINCE CHILDHOOD, say the flyers, but there's hard-headed adulthood in it too, with the Cheyenne Paddock horse-riding school and the coarse-fishing lake and the café-restaurant-diner and the western store and the big long bar and the caravan site and the beautiful log-built B&B bunkhouses all bringing money into the coffers. Above all there's the saloon, where Tony, the owner, draws crowds for six country concerts a week.

And what a saloon it is. It doesn't have saloon-girls – the only one is a shrilly Glaswegian resident line-dancer who has unfortunately been provided with an aerobics teacher's bum-pack microphone; amplified, her dulcet tones verge on the glass-shattering. But it has long refectory tables built out of old hardwood planking, with candles in bottles on top, and it has those huge wagon-wheel chandeliers hanging from the ceiling, eight or ten of them, quite a sight. There's an amazing set of stuffed heads – an inapposite kudu or two, sure, but also a buffalo, dominating the whole thing – and an equally impressive set of murals, western scenes, painted in every possible corner like tattoos on an all-over fetishist. Above, a series of portraits display various versions of the southern/ western/ Country and Western male archetype: Rhett Butler, Johnny Cash, Dwight Yoakam and Garth Brooks; the King, the Duke and Country Willie; the Good, the Bad and the Outlaw Josey Wales.

It looks built to have a fight in, and there is a half-time shootout for the local gunfighters; but in spite of them, and the sign saying NO INDISCRIMINATE GUNFIRE, we have an uproariously peaceful evening. Agnes, drinking Bacardi out of a plastic bottle in her handbag, tells me about being left behind on a pilgrimage-cum-bus-trip to Daniel O'Donnell's hotel in Donegal. Jackie, a listener and not a dancer, wants to know about the British bands that are doing well on the circuit. Jackie's wife Audrey trumps my Singing 'ammer with jovial tales of a Belfastman called the Singing Brickie, whose fans have been known to turn up wearing yellow crash-helmets and carrying hods, and a rural Irishman called the Singing Farmer, who regales the Belfast clubs with songs about Mad Cow Disease.

I ask her why she had to bring my ex-wife up just when I was having a good time, and it goes down well, but it's the tears of a clown in reverse; I am deep in what I hope is the final pre-divorce wrestle. Things are particularly fraught since Jolene and I have recently announced our intention to pioneer our way north and – finding our own patch of land to build a dream on, our own Trailsend – move to the seaside with the children. We dream up the scheme one Sunday morning, lazing around, and it gets a hold of us; to get away from the south-east, to get away from Ruby and from Jolene's ex-husband, to get away from the past; above all to strike out where our lives can't be intruded on whenever someone else's life doesn't come up to scratch.

I put the scheme to Ruby with a Pilgrim Father's wide-eyed enthusiasm, and manage to persuade her that it's not working out as things are, that the children will be better away from the south-east, where neither of us has ever belonged, that if she has the children for long weekends, and for complete weeks in the holidays, it will make for better contact than the stop-start stuff she has at the moment. And after some justified huffing and puffing she agrees, and we put the house on the market; and though she takes it off the market for a bit without telling me, I speak to her again and she agrees again, and we get an offer for the house for more money than it's worth from a solicitor who wants to put a hard-standing where the rose-garden is, and I can't say I care all that much how bad a year next year might be for those bloody roses.

There's just one, or maybe two more times when Ruby gets into reverse about all this, but it doesn't cause serious problems, save for a panic when Jolene and I are about to complete the buying of our big tall house in a town on the coast, and Ruby suddenly insists on all our financial dealings being watertight before she'll agree to the package; since her idea of water-tightness includes me handing over a good bit of what's suppos-edly going to be mine in order to insure her against something going wrong with the deal, it's my turn to be not too happy. But in the end I manage to get off the barrel she has me over and it all gets through on time, with me fielding calls from lawyers and from those further up the chain, and driving documents from one solicitor to the other, and buying a bottle of Grecian 2000 to make up for the ways in which it's aged me.

Of course, when we move, Ruby suffers; she suffers distance from the children, and she suffers not having me at hand to take it out on when things are not great for her. (At one point she rashly describes herself as feeling like she's 'howling like a wolf' for her lost children. 'Barking like a dog, more like,' I rashly and cruelly reply.) But once everything is signed, I feel nothing but a huge wave of relief that all that is over, and all my pussyfooting negotiating can come to an end; that I can now turn to her, like some pioneer of old, and talk about self-reliance and independence, having wrestled from all that's happened the prize of my own freedom. So what if the world of divorce is just a little world? It's still a world of hostility, a little world of frontiers you have to cross, and at a certain point, I realize, you have to not only take responsibility for whatever you yourself may have done; you also, I think sanctimoniously, have to make others take responsibility for their part in what happens to them. It's a hard truth that's difficult to say when you pride yourself on being reasonable; but at this point there's little left to say except that she fucked off, and that although there are other ways things could have turned out if I or she or he had behaved better or been more reasonable, she must have known from the start that it was possible she would come out, in her own mind, the loser.

Joe Piper's version of 'Margaritaville' has a mis-chorus, or a mis-chorus from what I remember of it. The real version has come into my head many times over the last few months: *Some people claim that there's a woman to blame/ But I know it's my own damn fault.* But when Joe Piper sings it, he sings it in a way that seems softer, and less in the reckless, Jimmy Buffett spirit of the thing, yet a happier chance as far as the here-and-now is concerned. *Some people claim that there's a woman to blame/ But I know it's nobody's fault*, it goes. And in the end that's what it's all about. All divorces – even those where someone's right and someone's wrong, even when someone's good and someone's bad – should be matters of responsibility; but not of fault.

One fight, and you're out...

'A friend of mine had a boy whom she brought up a Catholic,' says Agnes, back in Belfast, 'but she wasn't rigid about it, and she told him that when he was older he could choose his own faith; she wasn't making his mind up for him. Now – I think it was because of where they lived – she sent him to the local state school, the Protestant school. And when the Catholic boys from the Catholic school found out about it they used to give him a hard time; they used to come up to him and say, "Are you a Catholic or a Protestant?" And she told him to say to them, "I'm not a Catholic or a Protestant; I'm a believer in Christ." And of course when he tried it, they just said, "Well, that's all very well, but are you a Catholic or a Protestant?" If he'd said, "I'm a Muslim" or "I'm a Hindu" someone would have said, "Are you a Catholic Hindu or a Protestant Hindu?" – that's just the way some people want things to stay in this town.'

It's not a great time to be in this town or this province; there may, as Louis L'Amour once famously wrote, be a frontier in every man, but here there's a frontier in every town, maybe on every street. The 1996 ceasefire has just broken with the IRA bomb in Docklands and O'Brien, the baby-faced bomber with the *1984* surname, is about to blow an Aldwych bus up, and himself with it. Driving through County Armagh there is a line of people at a bus-stop, each wearing a white ribbon, a little shepherd's crook of cloth cut in the red-for-AIDS, green-for-Sinn-Fein, white-for-peace style. But when the senior school comes out and the boys are hanging round the chip-shop and the tobacconist's, every last one of them has a great smudge of black upon his forehead. Suffering from traveller's loss of time, from loss of contact with newspapers and with the time-scales of Fat Tuesday or British Summer Time, I haven't realized it is Ash Wednesday.

Soon everything begins to feel menacing. On the way to the High Chaparral, in Short's Club, there are checkpoints, with their towers of barred windows and barbed wire; there is the look on the faces of the gangs of boys on the street; even the weather – there's a gale blowing off the North Channel – threatens. We drift past the murals of west Belfast. On one, a slogan equates the position of Catholics in Northern Ireland with that of Native Americans. If the Republicans are the Indians, does that make the Loyalists the cowboys? Or – given the way so many of the westerners talk about all this stuff as their religion – is it a case of, 'Are you a Catholic cowboy or a Protestant cowboy?' And can you play cowboys and Indians when there are real guns out there on the streets?

At the High Chaparral, just as anywhere else, country club business is business as usual. The band is playing 'Don't Let Your Babies Grow Up to Be Cowboys', but some mothers do 'ave 'em, and that's just the way it is. The next night, at Newtownards – another town whose name one only knows from the *Nine O'Clock News* – the Colorado members assemble toting guns and ammunition and no one thinks it's strange to be doing this in the shadow of war. Quite the opposite. 'In this country,' a big woman called Ann tells me, 'you have trouble with religion. I work in a hospital; I've seen the troubles at first hand. When you go out for a night you have to forget all that. In *this* country,' she points at the band, the cowboys, the saloon-girls, 'you can forget those problems. One fight and you're out of this place. They all know that.'

Jackie – another Belfastman Jackie – finds it an escape, too. On his second Bacardi and Coke, he warms to the theme. 'Of course there's Catholics and Protestants mixed in here. But nobody mentions religion at country nights. You look around here,' he says, 'and the point is you don't know who anybody is; you just know their first names, or maybe you might know what it is they do, forbye. There's electricians, accountants, plumbers. That fella over there' – he points at a table of men with their backs turned towards the corner where we're squeezed in – 'he's one of them fellas that – what do you call them? – them fellas that do the headstones.' It seems fitting that, in these ceasefire days, he won't use the word 'mason', even with the qualifying 'monumental' in front of it. And if it's the guy in the middle of the group at the other table, then 'monumental' is quite appropriate, because he's hugely, unhealthily fat.

If the set of people crammed in here do come from both sides of the religious divide, then it is a triumph, because there is a feeling in the Northern Irish clubs that's not rivalled anywhere on the mainland; a feeling of family, of closeness, of location. All the clubs are within, say, thirty miles of Belfast, and you have the same faces appearing again and again – a little girl with red hair, a brilliant dancer and a crack shot at the High Chaparral shootout who, at the Colorado, has her plainclothes boyfriend along; another Agnes, who organizes a club at the British Legion in Whiteabbey, who tells a tale of travelling to California, meeting a couple there, travelling with them back to Nevada and ending up 'standing for them' at a hastily arranged cowboy theme wedding in Vegas. The dancing is busy and vibrant; when the Bar-Room Buddies play 'When the Bluebirds Sing', the couples smooch; when they play that old Smokey number about never getting used to not living next door to Alice, they go mad, sitting at their tables and shouting, in the middle of the chorus, 'ALICE? ALICE? WHO DE FOCK IS ALICE?'

Whatever divisions there have been, says Jackie, have benefited from C&W's own peace process, its own crossing of the frontier. A club was started in the Ardoyne, in the heart of Catholic west Belfast, on that side of the dividing line. But the committee of the Ardoyne Club didn't want to be seen only as a Catholic club, so they invited the committee of the Abilene, Jackie's own club, to their opening night. 'We expected just to be left to ourselves at best,' says Jackie. 'At worst we were a wee bit frightened about what we were getting ourselves into. But the Ardoyne committee got up in a block and they came across that dance-floor to our table and each one of them shook hands with each one of us. They made us welcome. And we had a great night over there.' It's how the west Belfast was won – without a shot fired. Now O'Brien and his friends were threatening to throw it all away, send those little white ribbons to fly away in the wind like so much tumbleweed.

Jackie has to get up; he has to carry the Abilene flag for the Trilogy. ('I get it made by the guy as does the flags for the Twelfth of July,' says Jackie, but he means it practically, not significantly.) The Trilogies in the Belfast clubs are moving; everybody but everybody in the hall joins hands and participates, belting out the 'Glory, Glory', unironically observing the lowering and the raising of the flags. The pistols are raised and fired; there's a huge volley of shots, and such is the feeling in the hall, in this community, that thoughts of sectarian ceremonies – of Republican funerals or Loyalist parades – do not even cross my mind. And then the lump in my throat turns into a bit of an obstruction, because it emerges that the Belfast Trilogy is not just a trilogy; here in the Ards Rangers Social Club, and almost everywhere else in Ulster, they play 'Glory, Glory', yes, but then they tack 'God Save the Queen' on the end. I play dumb and keep quiet and mime singing, since people are watching. 'Don't worry,' says Agnes, 'it's just like what they used to do in the cinema. People just follow it as a formality.'

I'm reassured by that, but as I look about the hall my eye comes to rest on a man standing in the Trilogy line. As he sends her victorious, happy and glorious, he begins to raise his right hand in a definitively Loyalist gesture of no surrender, and everything Jackie and Agnes have been saying seems to go out

the window for a moment. But then another hand snakes out –
that of the man beside him – and pulls the first man's hand
down. The first man's hand goes up again; the second man's
hand pulls it down. The first man's hand goes up a third time;
the second man's hand pulls it down. I watch the two of them
come off the dance-floor at the end. And it turns out that the
second man is a cowboy; that the peacemaker is a fully armed
honcho with two guns and a sixteen-inch knife at his belt. But
the first man is not. He has the tight, cropped face and hair of
an Orange marcher. He is wearing a brown shirt and tie, and
for a hopeful moment it looks like his, and not the cowboy's, is
the historical uniform.

CHAPTER SEVEN

Don't Take Your Guns to Town

Shooting towards the Boot Hill end . . .

Bless me, Father, for I have sinned: once, I killed a man.

It isn't the Greek who gets it, unfortunately; it's a man called the Marshal. It happens at the Lone Rock, Roche, which is where I first learn to handle a gun, albeit a replica, albeit a borrowed replica, albeit a borrowed replica that the owner has to help me buckle on, albeit a buckled-on borrowed replica that the owner has to teach me how to shoot. Curiously, the owner–instructor is the Marshal himself; an existential cowboy from an avant-garde western, he participates in his own destruction, conspires to bring about his own fate.

It's the Marshal who takes me out into the car-park of the football club where the Lone Rock meets. Around the ground, the landscape is commanding; on three sides of where we are there are the tall cliff-walls of the china clay works; they're grey, but were they red they'd be perfect as a backdrop for the Seventh Cavalry to make a tumbleweed reconnaissance in front of. A motley crew of desperadoes is assembled for a face-to-face, quick-on-the-draw, one-man-against-another scenario. There are the professionals: the Marshal himself, (Big) Jim, a smart gambler in black. There are the semi-pros: a couple of other kerchiefed or stetsonned regulars, including Kenny, the dump-truck driver who's broken down. And then there's me, a first-timer, and my main hope of not being completely humiliated, Jim's nine-year-old daughter, the girl who told me the Cornish myths of Tregeagle and Dozmare. But as we stand together she takes, from her ladylike handbag, a ladylike pearl-handled miniature in a ladylike white holster. I go weak at the knees.

I watch the first two combatants walk to opposite ends of the gravel surface and turn to face each other. The judge, another combatant, calls out a random set of figures – FOUR! EIGHT! TWELVE! THREE! – before suddenly arriving at an agreed signal – FIVE! – upon which the duellists draw and fire. The gunshots echo around the bleak emptiness of the darkening evening; and my interior laugh is just as hollow-sounding as the Marshal straps me in a holster and gives me a quick coaching course. I'm amazed to discover that it really does work just like it does in the movies. The quickest way to shoot is not by cocking it back and then pulling the trigger, but by pulling the trigger and, keeping it pulled, fire with a wild, risky slap across the cocking mechanism; 'fanning', it's called, or, in my case, perhaps, fannying.

I'm relieved to know that the shooting bit is as simple as that, but then one of the gunfighters – Black Widow or Preacher, possibly – complicates matters. 'Sure they're blanks,' he says reassuringly, 'and sure the gun-barrels emit only a small spark' – the barrels in this part of the world are blocked up and then have a tiny hole drilled in them – 'so there's no real danger.' But while the spark hardly renders the replica pistol a lethal weapon, the spark can do some damage at close quarters. For that reason, he tells me, I have to avoid shooting while the gun is still pointing through the holster; and I have to avoid doing a 'buckle-shot', which is firing before the gun is fully upright. In my state of heightened tension – already aware that I'm more maladroit than a puppy-fat nine-year-old and a heartbroken truck-driver – I can't decide which of these two humiliations I'd rather endure – to shoot myself in the balls, or to achieve the rare feat of shooting myself in the foot metaphorically and literally at the same time.

Finally it comes round to my turn. I trot out a tad uneasily on my boots up to the far end. I'm all set, I think, but then the man in black appears and, with an inside-leg joke, a tailor's wisecrack, ties my lace up for me. (Even the little girl knows how to do *that* for herself.) The Marshal and I agree on the number four and, readying myself, I look up and stare him in the eye, as one is no doubt supposed to do. The numbers start – THREE! SIX! ELEVEN! – and then, and only then, as I gaze down the barrel of my borrowed gun, do I realize what lies on the fourth side of Roche Football Club's ground. It's the local cemetery, for Christ's sake! I am shooting towards the Boot Hill end.

The numbers continue, carrying me on towards the fateful – the fatal? – moment. ONE! TWO! NINE! My hand twitches. My brow frets. Is my number to be up? When FOUR! finally arrives, not only does my gun go off – in roughly the direction in which the Marshal is situated – but my heart goes off too. For only one shot rings out, and when I look up I see the Marshal standing in the club floodlights looking at his gun and cursing the mechanism, a good workman thoroughly pissed off with his tools. But what of that? I shot the sheriff! I stride towards him, offering my newly acquired pardner's handshake. 'Best of three,' he mutters, with a Jack Palance smile. And in episodes two and three of the Marshal's life-story his arm was better-poised and his six-shooter better-oiled. Both times my Colt 45 had not even left the leather pouch at my side before I heard the crack and lay, figuratively at least, boot-soles up in the Cornish dirt.

You have to be in what we call the kill position . . .

George, on the other hand, I do not get the chance to shoot against. In terms of gunslinging, George occupies a different ether.

George is a jolly sort of bloke with greying hair cut in a

181

youngish style, an open, impish face and one earring. I meet him by accident, not knowing who he is, at the Rocky High Club, which happens in an ex-servicemen's joint at Chiddingfold, a commuter-belt village in deepest, greenest Surrey. The night I am there it's their pre-Christmas American Supper and the place is full of westerners; the Texas Drovers are out in force in one corner, the Santa Fe people in another; the Pistoleros have rifled a whole table, the Dixie Rebels have usurped one too. I talk to Rowdy, a house-husband from Aldershot with a stagecoach in his garage, and Raymond, a well-off Brookwood bloke with Civil War cannons in his. George is sitting on the door, all jollity, greeting the incomers, selling raffle-tickets and facing down an extraordinary heap of buffet food (scotch eggs, sausage rolls, pork pies, ham sandwiches) piled high on his plate. It does not look like training-camp food for a serious gunslinger, but nevertheless George, an ex-truckie bus-driver from Cranleigh, is Britain's Quick-On-The-Draw champion.

George invites me to visit his shooting club, which meets every Thursday in a ropy Scouts' hut in Shalford, near Guildford. It's the backside of a wealthy village on the edge of a wealthy town; the walls are scuffily scruffy, and if the tables are white it's only because they've been whitewashed that afternoon. The heating is from a huge gas-burner that looks like the inside of a jet engine and makes my clothes stink of butane. George, in the know, has left his western finery at home tonight. At Chiddingfold he was dressed like a gambler, in the slinky blacks and silvers of a Mississippi card-shark, but tonight he's in jeans and an M&S-type bottle-green collared sweatshirt with a Golden Eagle motif and an AMERICAN DREAM logo.

BANG! The firing begins behind us and peppers our conversation with a sharp, acrid punctuation. The men in the club all have their own weapons; what about him? 'I've got a range,' he says. 'Some replicas, some real.' He rhymes off the great western names, the American dreams, that sit in his pistol collection: Colt, Peacemaker, Remington. 'I've also got a Winchester and a flintlock. The Winchester's the old-fashioned Kentucky-type rifle, for when I dress mountain-man or Indian. The flintlock means I can dress Indian right back to pre-1750s, to when the Spaniards first came over and the Indians would capture one or two of these things. It's a right distinctive bit of gear. Believe it or not, I got it at a car boot sale – I bought two and out of the two I made one good one. They don't fire, but they look the business.'

Looking the business is clearly a big part of the game; though you have to know your business, too. 'There's two basic types of gun the gunslingers like us use. There's a sideblast gun – what most of these are here' – he hands me a pistol to hold, and shows me the gap between the barrel and the tube – 'so when it's held with the barrel pointing forward, you'll see a little blast come out, about a foot either side. But in Scotland, for instance, they tend to use the other sort, what's known as a throughblast, where the spark comes out through the front of the gun.' This is what I used in Cornwall, then. 'Now that could obviously,' says George, not much to my relief, 'be dangerous. If a bit of the metal came out of the gun and flew down the barrel it could come out and embed itself. If two fighters are up man-to-man then one could actually feel the blast or get a powder-burn on his clothes if things go wrong. In America they actually have a screen they put between the two people.'

The firing is going on apace in the huddle of men in the centre of the hall. What's there is all the equipment you need for a British Association of Gunslingers-approved competition. There's some pretty high-tech stuff, with a very delicate computerized timer wired to an eye-level sound-and-vision thing. Before the fighter's eye a red light comes on. He calls ready and the light goes off. Next time the light comes on – any time up to ten seconds later – he must draw and fire, and the sound bit of the equipment measures the swiftness of his response. There's low-tech, too. At the fighter's side is a balloon on a stand, round about waist-level off the ground. The fighter sets the right level for himself before he starts, like a high jumper making a mark, with a dummy draw. The gun has to be alongside the balloon for the spark to burst it; it's the test that the bullet would have gone somewhere near the imaginary opponent. Don't burst the balloon and you'll be called a foul and given a 100 – a whole second, which puts you about as far behind the likes of George as George would be behind Jesse Owens over 100 metres; or as far as the likes of me would be behind Jesse James. 'The balloon's there to make you adopt the right posture,' says George. 'You have to be in what we call the kill position.'

BANG! We watch the fighters working out for a bit. There's a man called Colin who has two Sharp's rifles. Since he works at British Aerospace and therefore has what George calls 'his own private rifle range' (whether the relevant Ministry considers the airfield Colin's property is another question altogether), he's able to use real ammunition from time to time. A father-and-son combination arrive in a B-reg Datsun, the Confederate flag stuck firmly to their bumper. Both are wearing identical black Indian-motif T-shirts. The son has an elastic bandage on his elbow, testimony to the fact that there really is such a syndrome as Gunslinger's Elbow; *The Lancet* take note. I make a weak joke about it but George doesn't find it funny. Instead he launches into a description of the way that tension can affect a gunfighter's shoulder at the moment of firing. He stands up and demonstrates rapt body followed by a jerky exit of gun from holster; seen this way, the professional way, it looks like an orthopaedic nightmare.

Has he ever suffered? No; not even at the Championship, which happens yearly, in North Devon; it's a well-known C&W place, the Farmer's Tavern, situated in a seaside trailer-park at Brean Sands. Three hundred-odd people were in for it the year George won. On the first couple of days the field is reduced by a sort of qualifying competition; like an Olympic event, it's an against-the-clock affair initially. 'They have a cut-off time,' says George, 'like, say, four-four. Four-four is 0.44 of a second, less than half a second. You go up there and your fastest shot out of three is the counter. If you do five-oh, five-oh, four-four it still means you qualify for what they call Supercats.' Needless to say, George qualified. The technique is the fanning one – the sweep across the hammer with the gloved hand, in classic Wild West style – which meant that a friend of George's who has only one hand did not qualify, though six others made it to the last day shootout from the original field. 'You'll find that various area champions are there,' says George, 'the Welsh champion, the Scottish champion, the area champions. The year I won there was Lonesome; he's the Scottish champion, and had won it the year before. There was Johnny Yuma, from the Midlands. Johnny Ringo; he's London-based. And Polecat, from the Isle of Wight.

'It's not easy to go up to that line. It's just on the day. You look at these blokes here, in this hall, doing four-four. I couldn't do four-four here, now, on that machine. But you put that trophy up there, and it's different. It's pressure. There's adrenalin pumping, there's all that. I'm lucky – I'm one of these people who gets calmer under pressure. You take Colin over there – he's terrible. Once the pressure's on for Colin his knee shakes.' Colin, hearing himself talked about, joins us. George describes a man called Trapper Dan, who gets so into watching the light he just can't fire. 'He gets so into it, so into it, he's watching that line . . . and when that light comes on, he's still watching it – he knows he's got to do something but he can't remember what it is. He can't move, he's froze.'

'There's a bloke on the Isle of Wight,' says Colin. 'He's been top dog on the Isle of Wight for a very long time; he's called Crazy Horse. He's got arthritis now – it's a shame, he can't shoot as well as he used to do. But on his holster, down below where you have the lace to tie it to the leg, he used to have a little cow-bell attached. And if he was standing here like this, with us talking, you would hear nothing. Nothing at all. But when he stood up there at the line – well, you could hear that bell

doing this –' He mimes a leg shaking a bell. 'So when he pulls –'
'You've just got to get that twitch at the wrong time,' says
George, 'and you're gone. When you're up there, you know, the
adrenalin's pumping, your hand's shaking – but if you touch
the gun accidentally because your hand's shaking and you don't
step back, you'll be called a foul. You're not allowed to touch
your gun, or your body – everything's got to be so that you can
see light. There's a guy who stands behind you who we call the
bucket judge because this' – he points to the holster – 'is the
bucket.' George rarely has problems with the judges; in fact, it
sounds as if George has a perfect sporting temperament. 'When
I get up to the line, I'm completely calm, ready. Then, once it's
over, once my foot comes off that line, it doesn't matter how cold
it is, I bust out sweating – win, lose or draw. But before it, there
I am, I'm rock-steady, do the job. It's when I get off – that's when
I go to pieces.'

At Brean, the final arrived. After a draw – they pull cards, of
course – Lonesome went up at number four with George at
number five. 'Lonesome went up before me,' says George, 'and
he did three-eight-point-two, three-eight-point-two, then three-
nine dead. Now in the final it's the total that counts; not just
the one shot, like in the qualifying. And I went up there next, and
I did three-nine, three-eight-point-two, three-eight-point-one; I
was one-thousandth of a second up on him. Well, Johnny Yuma
went up and then Johnny Ringo, but neither of them matched
it. There was a great round of applause and you could virtually
feel the tension leave that room. It was all over. I'd done it. And
there was a pause for a moment, but then that man, Lonesome,
came virtually all the way across the room and he shook my
hand in front of everybody. And he said, "Well done, George.
Brilliant, mate." And then he smiled, and said: "Next year you're
mine."'

Back in the Scouts' hut, I go up and have a go. I have five
shots, and even having had George coach me in the flowing
movement he instils in all his disciples, I can still only get to

point-seven something. I retire gracefully and leave the floor to George. He takes on a retired bank manager who only took up gunslinging three months ago. Over three rounds, the difference between the expert and the novice is not distinguishable by the ear alone. I mention this to George and he says, 'You're right. It's tiny differentials. The difference here doesn't much count – we're just fooling about. But you take the difference between me and Lonesome. One-thousandth of a second. You need the computer to detect that, you need all that equipment just to work out who's on top. But more important than that – in real life, we'd both have been dead.'

Are there any more real cowboys?

Are those tears in my eyes, or are my contact lenses just playing up?

I am driving the van along the Leeds Road into Huddersfield listening to Willie Nelson duetting on Neil Young's *Old Ways* album, asking if there are any more real cowboys still working on the land. Here, in the west of a county that hugs the cold east coast, it's hardly a western landscape. The outskirts of town are greyly northern, with sooty two-up two-downs, re-pointed and re-windowed, lining the gently sloping roads up to the moors; the land of Ian, not Sheriff, Brady. The main drag does have an American look, though it's the America of today, not that of Hollywood myth. An endless line of car showrooms mobs the road, just as on the outskirts of Nashville; there's Ford and GM-Vauxhall – the dying giants of the American trade – but more visible are the gleaming lines of Japanese models that the Americans hate yet buy: Daihatsu, Toyota, Mazda, Mitsubishi.

I am in search of Bob Dixon. I know he lived in a village called Golcar, on the outskirts of Huddersfield, and everything seems to be conspiring to lead me to him. The Renault dealership is a Dixon's, there's a Dixon's white goods store in town and, turning a blind corner and finding myself lost, I see that I am wedged uneasily between Huddersfield Funeral Supplies and Dixon's Old-fashioned Ice Cream. None of these is the right Dixon, of course, and I don't find Golcar this first time. It is a place to which signs point; but as soon as you get to where the signs point to, they have already begun to point back. All I find is a tombstone-like rock-heap up above me, and a place called Cliff End.

Lost, I give up for the moment. Deep in *Last of the Summer Wine* country, I eat a cowboy lunch of beans and bread and wander round the Bamforth dirty postcard museum before wandering into the tiny local office of the *Colne Valley Chronicle*. A nice, jolly girl with a broad smile digs me out a photocopy of the issue of 30 December 1994. I glance at the headline as I go back to the van: WHY DID COWBOY BOB – ONE OF THE GOOD GUYS – HAVE TO DIE?

The Spirit of the West

I had come across JB's city by accident, knowing no more about it than a couple of tourist-brown road-signs pointing me first down a B-road, then down a local road, then down a rough ash-and-pebble composite towards an uncertain destination. After a while, I had found, the sensible signs peter out into gaudy things about go-kart racing, but at the end of the rough road is an even rougher car-park, a barely bulldozed shapeless waste of red ash and rock, with parking divisions roughly made from chunks of painted half-bricks.

But beyond can be seen the odd but neat outlines of low, wooden buildings signed as stores and saloons and jails and long, outlined ranch-houses. I can see, through the fence, a prairie patch, a shooting-gallery, a Wells Fargo coach sitting horselessly under a wooden awning and a gunsmith's shop with a glass case of pistols gleaming vaguely inside. It is, in short, a full-size replica of a western town, ten times the size of Trailsend. But it is also a ghost town; there's no sign of life, no one in the admission booth to take my money and no one at the gate to stop me entering.

As it is a summer Saturday I'm confused; the gates creak as, uninvited, I walk in and look around. Hearing voices, I begin to make a long walk across the pebbled courtyard towards a long, low canteen. My boots crackle loudly on the stones and a rock or two bounds melodramatically across the empty waste. Just as I am half-way over, I hear the hollow echo of other boots on gravel. The only thing that's missing is the jingle of spurs, the sound of a pistol being cocked; for when I turn slowly around a man in full cowboy gear – checks, suedes and boots – is standing there. His legs are apart in classic western posture. Maybe he asks me what I was doing in this man's town, says I'm where I don't belong, stranger; but probably he tells me, with a nice smile, that they are shut on Saturdays, and suggests I talk to JB, the owner – 'A man with a story to tell,' he says.

I go over to the café and introduce myself. For a man with a story to tell, JB is nothing much to look at at three o'clock on a Saturday afternoon. He's in what passes for mufti among these people – a black Indian logo T-shirt and jeans which mean that his long hair and droopy moustache look more heavy rock than Lone Rock. I chat with him a bit. He talks about Colt 45s and Winchesters – Widowmakers, he calls the pistols – invites me to come back later and lets me camp on his land. What fuller invitation could there be? For the rest of the afternoon I sit amongst a Bank Holiday crowd in a small, hilly town called Wadebridge, where an all-woman troupe of morris dancers is drowning out a weedy male busker who offers uptempo versions of 'Streets of London'.

Perhaps it's that that drives me back too early; the show has not yet begun. JB has promised a Wild West reconstruction featuring men and women (but especially men) dressed up as outlaws, sheriffs and hillbillies; and engaged in bank robberies, abductions, sieges and shootouts; in short, the Hollywood version of the west in which baddies and goodies battle it out for power or money or love. JB smiles wryly when I point out – as so many have pointed out to me – that this world of face-to-face confrontations is not a true reflection of the old west. He agrees, says they pull in the punters, points to the fact that there's a paradox; people like him are initially drawn to the cowboys by the movies, but by the time they have read anything about the real cowboys they have to despise the John Wayne depiction of things.

But it goes further than that in his case. He says that he insists that the goodies always win in his shows. 'It's not something you can show the young,' he says, 'having the evil triumph.' Not when you're a dead ringer for Wild Bill Hickock you can't, and live as him in your head; not when you're trying to build a new England (or is it a New England, an American dream?) in the far south-west of the existing one; and not when what's happened to JB has happened to you, you can't. Well, not if you're JB, proprietor of the brand-name The Spirit of the West.

Cowboy Bob draws, and fires . . .

Back in the north-east, you can imagine it; the skeleton staff on duty at the *Huddersfield Examiner* that night wouldn't expect so huge a local story as Cowboy Bob dying in the streets of Golcar coming off, not on Boxing Day, in holiday time. So the initial reports of that cold December Wednesday are vague and sketchy.

They run like this: Robert Dixon, forty-four, a former soldier known locally as an eccentric obsessed with the Wild West, is seen in a street near where he lives firing off a pistol at one o'clock in the morning. His neighbours know Bob is a quick-on-the-draw expert; the local paper has reported his being five times London fast-draw champion. He's also known as harmless, as better than harmless, as a man who goes shopping for old folks, who's organized pool and darts marathons for Children in Need, who's advised local councillors on where to site wheelchair ramps; and he should know, because – poor Bob, ONE OF THE GOOD GUYS, remember – he looks after his crippled wife who's almost bedridden, who's dying from cancer, who's on morphine to ward off the pain of all her terrible diseases.

So after he fires the shot, it isn't hard for the police to find out where he lives; everyone knows. The local PCs call out an Armed Response Vehicle crew who get to the house, one of the grim, squat bungalows that make up Maple Avenue, sometime after three in the morning. All the lights are off. At ten to four the ARV men see a curtain twitch, and they're alert. They prepare themselves, take up positions. Soon after, the door opens and there's an exchange of shouts; curses on one side, warnings on the other. The door closes again. A few moments later, it opens again. There's more shouting, more cursing. Cowboy Bob suddenly draws and fires two shots from his silver pistol. He misses. The ARV PCs fire back. They don't. Cowboy Bob crawls back into the house, where's he's found to be dead as earth, and the matter is left in the hands of the Police Complaints Authority.

Drop your guns, or I'll drop you . . .

At JB's city it has started to drizzle; the promised show is threatened. The twenty or so people around stand huddled on the front-porch step watching the water drip down, desperadoes waiting not for a train but for better weather. Not all are cowboys; Bob – another Bob, all specs and middle-aged spread – has turned up wearing the uniform of the US Marines. It turns out he has a dream to set up an American Forces display in the field next to JB's town and has a collection of tanks and jeeps he's going to donate.

He's a pleasant bloke who, like the rain, drips hints of a tantalizing past. He claims to have been in the British Army most of his life; but to have been 'seconded', first into the Foreign Legion, then to the US Airborne in 'Nam. Of course I have no grounds to disbelieve him. Nor do I have any grounds to disbelieve him when he tells me that, at some level of his ancestry, a male of his lineage married into the Cheyennes, meaning that he was suckled by a full-blooded squaw. As the rain eases he wanders out on to the gravel courtyard, and picks up a tomahawk which has been left around for anyone who fancies a throw at the hunk of log that's the target; and it takes him four goes to get it to stick in.

The show does happen in the end; it's performed by the junior section, the Young Guns, a group of twelve- to fifteen-year-olds permanently or temporarily resident in JB's city and who include JB Junior and a girl with cerebral palsy whose wheelchair is completely integrated into the show. The Young Guns have written their own script, in which an outlaw abducts an Annie Oakley type and wounds the Marshal who comes to her aid before the Marshal hopalongs his way to bloody victory. The dialogue suggests that Hollywood's other genres have got to them: 'Drop your guns or we'll drop you,' one shouts, more Rambo than Duke, more van Damme than van Cleef. The goodies take a bow; the baddies, duly dropped, get up and take a bow too.

We all go inside. This is the first evening show promoted by JB's new organization, COWBOY – the Confederation of Western Buddies of Yesteryear. It's envisaged that this will have a wider membership than it has at present; for now the members are JB's resident compadres. I chat with a few, and each insists obliquely that I get to grips with JB's story; each drops hints of some big tale. Peter, a rangy, lanky, white-haired man who works in Argos in Swindon for eight months of the year and joins JB in the summer, breathes in my ear about his having 'recaptured' the place. Bob the Foreign Legionnaire mentions a sum of money – £400,000 – though what I'm supposed to understand by that, I don't know. As the evening goes on the figure grows and the detail becomes simultaneously more specific and more sketchy. 'JB was half a million down,' says someone else. 'Lost about £700,000, so they say.' Peter the Wiltshire Warehouseman comes top with £800,000, but his triumph is only temporary; an American naval base engineer takes me for a walk and tells me dark things about paintballing, all-terrain vehicles and masonic conspiracies at the heart of Cornwall County Council: 'They say a million flew away out of this place.'

As these Chinese whispers fly I become aware that the presence of my notebook seems to bring disconcerted frowns to people's faces. JB himself gives me a distrustful look and I show him that I was just writing down his COWBOY acronym. The camp restaurant-runner gives me an odd look across the food counter. Peter asks me suspiciously if I used to work for *Westerner* magazine, and I say I've never heard of it. John, who's got an efficient, maybe officious, tidily sober manner born of working at Porton Down (actually he says he worked on the civilian side at 'an MoD establishment in Wiltshire'), says that The Spirit of the West's westerners are a bit nervous; there's talk of court cases.

The concert begins. The singer is a seriously lonesome local guy with a nice woo-woo in his voice and no time for Garth Brooks, so I collect my half-bottle of whisky and a tea-cup from the camper and park myself at a table. I watch JB officiate. He's a bundle of fund-raising energy; now he's raffle-ticketing, now he's orchestrating an auction, now he's letting a pair of old women finger his suede trousers ('I always say they're even softer on the inside'). Twenty quid is the price of a Japanese therapeutic massage from Bob the Legionnaire's pretty wife, and JB makes a great play of having it in public, uttering a series of Kenneth Williamsesque groans. The masseuse looks none too pleased at the cheapening of her art – perhaps JB doesn't know what Bob has told me, that she's a karate black belt – but she gets on with it gamely enough.

For JB, it's money in the bank; for everyone else it's a good evening. By half-eleven everybody's well on, particularly a long-haired bloke called Two Sheds, who says he's living in the Indian tepees I'd been warned not to park my van too near; he'd like to talk but he's out of his tree on bourbon he's drinking from a silver pocket-cup. I pick up my tea-cup and my whisky bottle and begin to – rather unsteadily – cross the gravel. I look round at the building I've just left and catch sight of JB sitting on the verandah. All that's visible is his Hickock moustache and his cheroot – or his Silk Cut, I can't be sure – glowing in the darkness. I call out a good night. 'Good night, writer-man,' he drawls, and even in the dark you can see a little, ironic smile play along the edge of his lip.

He was swivelling a gun in his hand the way that cowboys do . . .

It takes an inquest to put flesh on the bones, to fill out the full horrible story; not just of what happened to Cowboy Bob, but of who he was, of what foul dust floated in the wake of his American dreams. When the coroner finally sits he orders the inquiry on the *Sound of Music* principle, with the beginning a very good place to start; and over a fortnight the whole tale unfolds, intentively, exhaustively, exhaustingly.

First up are those who spend the evening with Bob, who are in the Entertainment Centre on Boxing Day as Bob drinks his way through his daily ten-pint ration. The details are a bit pathetic; how he goes home to get his silver gun to proudly show a German visitor to the club, like a child bringing something in for the whole class to see; but ends up, as he gets drunker and drunker, trying to sell it for beer-money. How he tries to pick up a woman called Maxine, telling her that his wife is in a nursing-home (called Graceland, he says, with a rock 'n' roll touch), that he's all alone, that he wants to marry her; and how

Maxine refuses to let him walk her home – her step-son is with her – and Bob stomps off, 'upset and annoyed', round about midnight.

Bob gets himself out of lust's blind alley and turns instead into Sycamore Avenue. He's recovered his swagger, according to a man who looks up from his late-night Bank Holiday Clint movie to look out the window. 'He was swivelling a gun in his hand the way that cowboys do; spinning it round and round before slipping it back into his belt.' A witness hears a shot and phones 999. Whoever it is that reports him knows him and describes him as a 'nutter', and the comment is passed on to the armed officers who are then called out; of course they say such knowledge doesn't affect them; but if, for nutter, the phone-call had suggested he was a harmless fantasist, an American dreamer, well, maybe things might have washed out differently. But for now the nutter makes it home all right, and goes into the back bedroom, climbs into bed and, according to Maureen, his wife, falls straight into a deep, drunken sleep.

Maureen gets up a couple of hours later to go to the toilet; she's not bedridden actually, whatever Bob tells the women he's pursuing. She hasn't cancer, nor does she take morphine; she had an accident a few years back, and she has serious arthritis, but she can get around on her sticks, even if Bob, who has an allowance as her full-time carer, tends to spend the money on his ten pints at the Entertainment Centre rather than on her. She looks out the bathroom window and sees the intense brightness of the wall of light which the armed response people have set up to hide behind. Thinking that there are kids on the street mucking around, Maureen wakes Bob, who's known to have a temper; and he shows it now by snapping a pool cue in half before he goes out, shouting and swearing, to see what's going on.

And here the tales diverge, of course. Maureen, inside the house, hears little. She doesn't hear the police identify themselves, so when Bob comes back into the house, grabs his gun and says that he is 'going to settle it', she assumes he's going to give the muckers-about the mother of all frights, a shot across the bows. According to this version of things, Bob goes outside, and says either, 'Come into the light where I can see your face' or, 'Come into the light so I can blow you away.' The police, who say that they identified themselves, and that they warned him, and that he knew who they were, say he said, 'Come into the light so I can see you're coppers,' but even that, designed to show he knew they were, shows ambiguity. And Bob was known to have a uniform phobia; he cringed in a corner of the club once when an ambulance-man came in.

The answer never comes – not in words, anyway. PC 'C' – the armed responders are allowed to keep their anonymity – sees Cowboy Bob pull something from behind his right leg. And given that Bob has already ignored a barrowload of challenges – several policemen make a procession through the witness-box to establish how many challenges, and over how long a time Bob has been challenged – the officer is within his rights to act on 'split-second instinct' and, wishing to protect his fellow-officers and the bystanders who have come out of their houses, he shoots down the man who has just fired his gun twice in his direction. And how is he to know that Bob's beautiful silver pistol – unlicensed, unlike Thomas Hamilton's, and which he might have sold, earlier in the evening – is a quick-on-the-draw pistol, a sideblast one like George uses, like the ones hundreds and hundreds of displaced cowboys all over England use, and cannot hurt anything much bigger than a flea? Bob falls; no one told him that in this game they use real bullets.

I understood what it was like to lose it completely . . .

Next day is Sunday, and The Spirit of the West is open for business, so JB is up and dressed early; I see him when I slip round the side of the van for a pee at seven. Yes, he remembers;

he's got time to show me around if I come back at ten, ten-thirty. He's true to his word, and we see the saloon, the jail – 'proper cells and everything' – the bath-house. Everything looks like it's newly repaired, or not repaired, and J B is apologetic: 'There's a lot to do; most of it's superficial, but it's man-hours, you see.'

He takes me into his museum, where there's a stunning collection of western artefacts. Collecting is where it all started. 'I've always been interested in Americana, be it clocks, plates, uniforms, Zippo lighters, beers, bourbons, guns. I started with cowboy and Indian stuff and moved on. When we were kids we liked Hopalong Cassidy and I've still got Hopalong Cassidy watches and cap guns. It's how we won the west, as kids. What else was there to do for us, except win the west?' He leads me through the gun collection, which is a history of western firepower in itself; the walk is like watching rifles develop, just like walking through a Renaissance painting museum is like watching perspective grow.

'You start off with the Henry Rifle, which is 1865. Winchester bought out Henry and changed it by adding the forestock and changing the loading from the front to the gate; that became known as the '66 or the Yellow Boy, because it had a brass frame. Then came the '73' – he shows me different models, carbines, rifles, a change barrel, specifiying the change in gauge sizes – 'there's the '92, there's the '94, there's the '95, which Theodore Roosevelt used on all his hunting trips, there's the '97, with the pump-action –' And so on, and so forth, until my mind is boggling. 'But don't forget,' he says, 'that it's only Hollywood that made the Winchester the top gun. The reality was that Wyatt Earp carried a Smith and Wesson; Jesse James carried a Smith and Wesson. The average working cowboy would more than likely have carried a Smith and Wesson. They were cheaper. The Hollywood version of the west is rubbish. The job of this museum is to rescue the west from Hollywood.'

He has thousands and thousands of pounds' worth of Americana even though, when I meet him, he's never been to America.

'When I started you could pick it up very cheap, because the Americans were busy buying our furniture, and when they were busy buying our furniture I was busy buying their heritage. The last ten years the Americans have realized. There's two items here, for instance, that can't be priced. That original working saddle there, that's the very first working Texas saddle. That beaded waistcoat – I bought that as part of an Indian collection for five hundred pounds and ten years ago I turned down ten thousand for it. But what's the point of selling it? What's money?' He has silver inlaid spurs from the original Buffalo Bill Wild West Show. 'They went bust in England, you see. A lot of the stuff was sold off to get the troupe home. A lot of it was bought by Captain Edward Gray, who did shows under the name of Buffalo Bill the Second, and in the fifties his entire collection went to a British guy called Roy Montana; I met Roy in the late sixties and I inherited his stuff.'

That was long before he took to theme-parking. JB had set up an earlier Spirit of the West called Frontier City in 1978. He had built it, log by log, piece by piece, and it ran as a tourist attraction in the grounds of Peter de Savary's Littlecote Hall, near Hungerford. For reasons not quite clear but which were none the less heartbreaking, he had to leave and he took the city down log by log, piece by piece. He found a piece of land in Cornwall by going into partnership with a local man called Beazley. Log by log, piece by piece, he built the city again on the scrappy escarpment where I had found it. The deal that was struck ran something like this: JB would supply the expertise and the collections, Beazley would provide some of the land and look after the books, and something like equity of labour would be achieved to make the equity of reward a reasonable thing.

Things went on in roughly that fashion for a year or three. Beazley built himself a big house on the fringes of Frontier City, and JB built or bought himself one on the hill up above. (I had passed it on my way in; a rough sign of western-style wood had, in brand-coloured paint, its name, MONTANA PINES, etched upon it.) JB polished his guns, kept collecting; Beazley polished his calculators, kept accounts; until one time Beazley went sick, and JB was obliged to make sense of the books. What he found shocked him; far from being in a state of equity, he discovered that they were massively in the red, in debt to the bank; Frontier City was teetering over the edge. He toiled with the paperwork for a bit and came up with some figures; he struggled with them for a bit and then, his heart breaking a second time, decided to walk away. 'At the end of 1990, see – well, it was about February 1991 – I thought that was it, I'd had enough. I gave voluntary repossession to the bank. I thought, well, that'll have us straight with the bank if I just give everything back.'

But straight it didn't have them; for JB the nightmare was just beginning. The bank, according to JB, left Beazley in charge of Frontier City and in charge of turning a profit. Beazley, it seems, did his best, but his best involved every which tourist way; and you can see that the details still torment JB's lone prairie soul. 'They had jet-skis tearing round the lake,' he says. (It's a calm, reddish and coarse-fishable spot of water in the middle.) 'They had quad bikes running round the paths.' (These are western tracks peacefully criss-crossed by JB's horses.) 'They had paintballing around the town.' (This the town JB's hands had built from nothing on the scrap of empty land.) 'They lost the theme of the park – it just became a bit of this and a bit of that. Nothing to do with the west at all.'

For JB, the falling into disrepair of the fabric of Frontier City was the hardest thing to take. What work was done, he says, was badly done, without any of the sense of love or care or beauty that hangs over all JB's work; above all without any concern for authentication. As we tour he shows me examples of pine cabins mended with hardboard and MDF, of beautiful, authentic western paint-shades patched in DIY store imitations and scarred by paint-ball marks. 'It was just destruction,' he says. He shows little emotion as he talks about it; but to imagine him there, up in Montana Pines, stuffed in with the salvaged contents of the museum, which he'd never signed over, watching, log by log, piece by piece, his life's work being ruined; it's an extraordinary image, and the story, he says, almost had an extraordinary denouement.

J B watched the trippers and the tourists trash the place from his house on the hill for a couple of years, and then, in his own words, he flipped. 'I understand what it's like to lose it completely.' Viewed one way, it's inevitable; he was sitting besieged, as besieged as Cowboy Bob, in his house, with a den full of weaponry, and it was to his weaponry, and to the fantasy world of his childhood and his *alter ego*, that J B returned once the bright lights were shining in his eye. One morning he woke up with a purpose. He dressed himself in full western wear – hat, waistcoat, breeches – and saddled up his horse. He strapped on a pair of Colt 45s – Widowmakers, as he loves to call them – and stuck a Winchester rifle in his saddle holster. He mounted his horse and began to ride down towards Frontier City, bound for a showdown which would end with the bad guy dead and J B handing himself and his guns over to the local sheriff.

Of course, although he describes it as if it did when he's had a drink or two, it never really happened that way. Pressed, later, he clarifies: 'Of course I wasn't going to shoot anyone. When I said that it was a way of saying how I felt, how I might imagine it; not a way of saying what actually happened.' For J B has a family, a wife, a daughter, and they prompted enough of an internal voice to keep him in the twentieth century. Figuratively speaking, he turned his horse and went back home, back to Montana Pines. Instead of involving himself in a bloody showdown, he began to imagine one; over the following weeks he began plotting out a western novel. 'More a set of short stories,' is how he describes it. By the sound of it it's a work in which the good end happily and the bad unhappily; for that is what fiction means, as J B wouldn't have it. In J B's world, here in the twentieth century, good triumphs over evil, and good and evil are clearly demarcated. 'When it gets published,' he adds, with a laugh, 'I'm going to put *Any resemblance to any characters living or dead is strictly intentional.*'

The story does not end there, of course, nor does it end unhappily. If anything, it ends uncertainly, with the talk, amongst Legionnaires who may or may not have been suckled by a squaw, of court cases that may or may not happen. Therapied by his writing, J B began the long and arduous process of winning back Frontier City through the courts, and Frontier City is now his again; his to rebuild and repair, log by log, piece by piece. (Beazley is living in Padstow, he thinks, and he is certainly not in clover.) There is a lot to do; not just to put right what was done by the jet-skiers and the war-gamers, but also to mend other damage, like that done to the paddleboat which used to ply the lake but which suffered a serious fire. J B's pardners join him for the summer and sleep in the jail or the saloon or the bath-house and put in the man-hours he badly needs, not just to repair, but to expand. He has a vision, as they say. 'It's coming right now. Phase One is back on its feet. The public are coming back. We're looking to the future. We've got outline permission for a massive country music-hall, where we can have big stuff; Johnny Cash should be playing here within two years. We want to make this place the Nashville of England. We've got a hundred acres,' he adds in a down-home voice, 'so we sure have got enough space.'

The only sadness lies in the loss of the name, which had to be changed in the face of bad publicity. Shaking his stetsonned head, he laments: 'I'm the creator and founder of Frontier City. I made that name up, and made the place's name. Yet I had to change the name because of them, and that still hurts; that's why we had to change it to The Spirit of the West.' He straightens himself up. 'But, as my father used to say – what goes around comes around. They got their comeuppance, the bad guys. Good prevails over evil. It's just that sometimes you begin to wonder how long it's going to take.'

We can't say if someone's dead or not . . .

Back in Sycamore Avenue, has good prevailed over evil? Is there
such a distinction as the gutter begins to run with blood? One
witness, who has been partying in Sycamore Avenue and goes
out to see what is going on, describes how, hit, Bob turns away
and walks back into the bungalow. 'You'd think he'd collapse
on the ground, but he didn't; he didn't even stumble,' he says;
he walked tall. Maureen has made it through the house on her
sticks, and, like a gunslinger's moll, is crouching over him,
shouting, 'I want to stay with him.' She's not allowed; the police
make her come out of the house. 'They made his wife climb over
his body,' says another bystander. 'She had to clamber all over
him, all the time screaming at the police to leave him alone.'

They didn't, of course; they followed the training manual,
which describes how the fatally wounded, in true movie fantasy
style, can sometimes manage to take one last pop at their assail-
ants. They reached the body quickly and removed the revolver;
and, even though Dixon was dead, they handcuffed his body.
'We're not medical experts,' one policeman says. 'We can't say
if someone's dead or not.' The paramedics arrive and say for
sure that he is, but the coppers leave the cuffs on. 'If we remove
them then we are interfering with the scene,' the same man
says. At the inquest, a plethora of senior officers form an orderly
queue and, one after another, offer reassuring statements about
how ARV incidents usually end peacefully, and praise PC 'C'
and his colleague, PC 'B', for displaying remarkable restraint.

Restraint? Maybe, but when the time comes, it seems, the
time comes. 'We open fire only as a last resort; we shoot at the
torso, never to wound or disable, because shooting at limbs does
not prevent a person from firing, whereas if you hit the torso
you inflict serious damage.' The Home Office pathologist reports
that Robert Dixon, forty-four, was killed by a bullet which hit
him in the chest and travelled through his body to the spine. It

damaged his main artery, causing massive internal bleeding. When the bullet hit the spine, he reported, fragments broke off, piercing his stomach and his liver, and a second bullet lodged in his pelvis. 'Shooting a gun out of someone's hand only belongs in films,' says the policeman. 'It's sheer fantasy.' The sad thing is that sheer fantasy was exactly where Cowboy Bob was living at the time.

From Brown to Blue . . .

> *We stood there in the courthouse-room*
> *So close yet far apart*
> *You brought along a lawyer*
> *And I brought a broken heart . . .*

But in the end it's not like that, not here, in this country; in the end a divorce doesn't amount to much in the head-to-head department. Sometime, pretty much out of the blue, an envelope arrives, looking pretty much like any other envelope, and inside there's a piece of paper that looks like the answer-sheet from a multiple-choice exam, only more poorly copied, and the District Judge who's written on it hasn't bothered to write in his best handwriting, hasn't even bothered to put proper ticks in the appropriate boxes, but just scrawled quick lines through the ones that say that the Petitioner (as opposed to the Respondent) has sufficiently proved the contents of the petition and is entitled to a Decree Nisi of Divorce (as opposed to a Judicial Separation) on the grounds of S.1(2)(a) of the Matrimonial Causes Act 1973, the adultery being with (as opposed to the co-respondent/ the party cited) a person unnamed, and that the date has been set for the pronouncement of the decree.

Not only do you not go, but you're not expected to go, and neither is your lawyer; the post or the fax or the legal telex will bring the news that the marriage is all but dissolved in a piece of paper that says that decree nisi has been granted. Then, six weeks later, it's all over. It's a bit more posh this time, with a red crown stamped on it to make it official, and it says that no cause having been shown as to why the decree nisi should not be made decree absolute, the said decree was made final and absolute and that the said marriage was thereby dissolved. And again, you're not there to see it happen, to see that moment. But you know it's not a country sort of moment, not a moment when

> The judge pronounced the words
> The way you wanted him to do
> He changed your name from Brown to Jones
> And mine from Brown to blue.

It's a queuing sort of moment, a pile-of-paper sort of moment, a rubber-stamping sort of moment.

So you're left with a piece of paper; and even if they say marriage is just a piece of paper, well, at least after a marriage you only have one piece, and it shows you're together; after a divorce you get one each, something for the files. Nothing much about it detains the eye, except at the bottom, where, in small letters, the decree says that were I to leave any money the divorce makes Ruby, in effect, dead. 'Property shall pass as if the former spouse had died on the date on which the marriage is dissolved,' it says.

Well – leaving aside the fact that at times in the last year certain consummations have been devoutly wished for – it's a nice thought that equates marriage with life and divorce with death. Of the marriage only the papers survive, and they're witness to the waste of time we've both endured. There's a huge file of all the letters and calculations and minutes and petitions; of letters abusive, rational, pleading, factual, scathing, pathetic; of official documents, drafted, redrafted, scored, initialled; of solicitor's bills, paid every month for a year, sometimes fifty, sometimes two hundred and fifty, and totalling, for a normal divorce-with-children which I worked hard to keep out of the lawyers' offices, well into four figures. And that's it; the marriage is over. And you have a choice; you can sit and you can brood over the fact that you got fucked over, and lied to, and cheated on, and did your own fair share of deceiving too; or, beyond the courtroom, you can decide that you're in a new country, and you can make your new land, you can cross the frontier and be wise and make sure it never happens again; you can make sure, after this struggle for selfish gain, that from now on you live in a commonwealth. And of course that's what you want to do; to understand that, in a different, a real sense, a wife is for life, not just for Christmas.

But one thing I know is this: twelve times this year my bank account will ring up a little credit from Ruby's funds; eighteen times in this coming year I must hand over, or collect my children, maybe from her flat, maybe from the motorway services; a hundred times this year the phone will ring, and it will be someone that I used to live with. Usually she'll just speak to the children, but sometimes she'll want me. I shall try to be patient, and understanding, and sympathetic; and she will try to be brave and resolved and understand how A led to B, how her desire to be away from me led, if not inevitably, then, as things turned out, away from the children; and sometimes she'll not understand that, and ring up to wail or moan; and I'll not be sympathetic, but scathing and fulsome in my condemnation, as I've often been before, and as I've no doubt often been in the moments I've described with perfect justification.

And we'll go round and round and round; it's a Circle Game.

What they need is a good knocking-over . . .

JB is a man with many postscripts; a man it's hard to say goodbye to. I see him for the last time on my way back to the van. He's being followed by a gaggle of ducks; more inhabitants of his city. It's sunny and he's smiling and the world seems in tune. The ducks he treats with the same affection as his compadres and his children and the visiting girl with cerebral palsy and all the visitors who come here. 'My new nickname they've given me since that Kevin Costner thing,' he says, 'is *Dancing with Ducks*.' And over at the tepees, where Two Sheds and his partner Diane dream of dancing with wolves, there's not a cloud either. 'This place has magnetism,' says Diane. 'I have a dream of living here. If at least in the holidays I can get down, that's fine. We'd have problems bringing the boys down here all year round.'

The boys are the three mentally handicapped young men that Diane and Two Sheds look after all year round; most of the year at Malvern, with summers in their tepees wherever the highway takes them. Two Sheds drives a big ex-army bus long enough to run the poles along the side of. It's the pace of life he enjoys: 'At home it's get home, switch on the electricity, cook with the microwave. Here you put on a pan of water and it boils – now it might take fifteen minutes, but if it does then you sit and think, remember how lucky you are to be where you are.' Two Sheds is sober now and he is apologetic to all and sundry, especially Diane. She is wearing Indian buckskins; he is in plain clothes now – a baseball cap, a checked shirt, cords, moccasins. His hair is grizzlier than I remember it from the night before and it's swept back, tied behind under the cap. He shows me round the tepees, tells me how they're erected, how the five huge poles are set up and stacked and wrapped around with canvas, how the fire-smoke waterproofs the inside.

Billy, one of the boys, appears; he's clutching, and waving like a banner, a pair of lurid blue underpants. 'Never a dull moment,' says Diane, telling him to put them away. Billy is in his thirties or forties; he has the mental age of a five-year-old. Alec, one of the other boys, appears and starts shaving. 'Is it your birthday?' hoots Two Sheds. The third is Eric, whose cerebral palsy is mild but whose development was set back, perhaps irretrievably, by being kept locked in at home throughout his childhood. Here, like the others, he roams free; in my days at The Spirit of the West I see him often, wandering, looking, greeting people, occasionally frightening them.

This is not all for Diane and Two Sheds. They also look after Simon, Diane's son, a physically handicapped fifteen-year-old who boarded at a special school until Diane, affronted at the way they were underestimating his capabilities, pulled him out and enrolled him in the local comprehensive. To do so she had to battle with the local Director of Education, and she had to battle with the DSS Tribunal for allowances and payouts. 'I'm a little spitfire when I get going,' she says. In the process she saw the world; saw the way that the caring bureaucracies wasted money while offering only pathetic living allowances to mentally handicapped people. Two Sheds chips in demotically: 'The Roths-childs of this world – the people who set these amounts – they stick an idea out and haven't a clue as to how it relates to the real world.'

They list some of their battles: how they had to take on the Council to get Billy's mobility allowance in such a form that they could buy a vehicle that would benefit all of them; how they had to take the Council on again when they tried to apply a 6 per cent levy to the paltry carers' allowances. They won on both counts, but only because they are free: 'I said to the Council,' says Two Sheds, ' "You can take away my house, because I don't need it." In this life, you need shelter and food, that's all. I can easily get food and' – he points around to the tepees – 'I have shelter. I can honestly say that I'd be happy as a tramp, as anything. I'm an ex-rugby player,' Two Sheds goes on, 'and I'm one of life's props. I prop people up – and I knock people over. And I try to make sure that the ones I knock down and the ones I knock over are the right ones. Some people need knocking over. If I have one thing to pass on it's that fact; that from time to time, lords, ladies, royalty even – what they need is a good knocking-over, no question about it.'

Here, in JB's New England, they take time off from their battles; here, in the world of goodies and baddies – as Two Sheds speaks, the gunfire from the Sunday shows begins – they can sit and watch the pan boil. But for all their proppery, for all their spitfirery, they welcome with a smile the families that trail through the tent, that gawp at the boys. A Manchester family arrives. The woman is a dimwit, a blonde bint in a straw hat and a short skirt. She has two boys in the United third kit, the silly blue and white one, and she has a husband who is most interested in the technical details that lie behind tepee-dwelling. 'Good design. Very clever,' he intones solemnly after each patient explanation from Two Sheds. He himself is not at all very clever and his initial suppositions are almost always wrong. 'Is that an Indian idea?' 'No, that's a Spanish stool.' 'Good design. Very clever.' The woman herself is interested only in the home-making aspects, and she punctuates the thick, smoky air with dialogue that suggests that the tepees are something that Laura Ashley whipped up that afternoon – 'Ooooh – you have a screen – so you can have a bit of privacy, like . . .' 'Oooh – look at that dog's bed – that's lovely, that.' Diane smiles her thin smile, and Two Sheds brews them a cup of his thick, black tea. The world is going by, and he's watching it, knowing what it's all about, knowing what's clever and what's lovely, and what's not.

A jukebox in the corner of my mind . . .

Bill, at the Western Star, would love to go to Nashville – 'Did you know they call East Anglia the Tennessee of England, there's so much country music around?' – but his wife won't fly, so this year they went to Scarborough. He's another septuagenarian cowboy, another man in black, though his black dancing-shirt has a lovely yellow rose motif across the shoulders and lapels. His haunt is the pretty rose-wound village hall in Boxford, and he's Suffolk through-and-through, with an east country twang in his voice so pronounced he sounds almost Australian.

Garner Tye sings a song about a man with a jukebox in the corner of his mind, and there's a jukebox in Bill's. He ain't no dancer ('That line-dancing – it's just one step forward, two steps back, ain't it?') but he claims to know the words of every song; he sits at home with a blank tape in the stereo and flicks it on whenever he likes the sound of an intro. He seems to like anything and everything. He likes Hank Williams, but he likes Willie Nelson, too; he likes cheating songs, he likes heartbreakers, he likes boozing and trucking and western and prison and lost highway numbers. (He's not indiscriminate: 'That "Achy Breaky Heart",' he says, 'isn't that the worst country song ever written?') But as we talk, and as we sing along together, it's clear that not a single line hits his life between the eyes, not a single lyric is a *they're playing my song* number.

He sits with a half of beer, but it lasts him the whole night, and he tells tales of his temperance at C&W weekends, where others do, but he doesn't. He's never driven the big rigs, or been in jail; he's stayed put here, in this pretty corner of rural England, and he worked fifty-one years less a week as an apprentice and a foundryman in the same heavy-cast propeller workshop; and even if his last years there brought methodological conflict with younger men trained in shoddier times, he was never unhappy in that 'Sixteen Tons' way. Above all, he's been married forty-six years to the sweet woman who sits next to him; he's never known the pain of separation.

We laugh about it for a bit, the total non-affliction of his life. *He*'s not dressing up to escape: 'All that happens is, you go to a festival, and by the end of the week, if you don't have *something* – a hat, a shirt, boots, *something* – you stand out as much as if you were doing a streak across Wembley Stadium.' Nor is he hiding; his 'If you go through a door marked "private", don't be surprised if you get thrown out' is a general, not a specific, warning. Yet all around is pain; Garner Tye is having to take half-sets off because, Bill says, he's lost half his voice and isn't sure if he'll ever get it back; and Terry, the organizer, is hocking a litre of Bell's whisky for a special raffle in aid of a local C&W-er who's fallen off a ladder and broken his back just at the time that his wife has been diagnosed as having leukaemia.

Bill and his sweet wife remain untouched, it seems. Garner Tye plays a Merle Haggard number called 'Holding Things Together', a weepie about a man bringing up his children alone, and I say, half-joshing, that that was *my* song. 'Not any more,' says Bill, 'by the look of you.' And tonight the bottle doesn't let me down; green number thirty brings me the bottle of Bell's, and I stick it in my backpack, thinking I'll sup some with the New Zealanders in the next combi back in the camp-site. I get up and shake hands with him. 'The Western Star motto,' he says, 'is *Arrive a Stranger, Leave a Friend.*'

At the camp-site, the curtains on the combi are shut and a laughter emanates that at the start of my journey would have left me feeling desolate. But now I just smile and fill a tea-cup with the water of life, and sit back. I don't quite know whether I've arrived, or have just left, or whether I'm just, like everybody else, in the middle of something; but I do know I'm not a stranger.